MULTILEVEL ACTIVITY & ACHIEVEMENT TEST BOOK

with CD-ROM

SIDE by SIDE

Plus

Life Skills, Standards, & Test Prep

BOOK 2

Steven J. Molinsky • Bill Bliss

Contributing Authors

Elizabeth Handley

Sarah Lynn

PEARSON

Longman

Correlation and Placement Key

Side by Side Plus correlates with the following standards-based curriculum levels and assessment system score ranges:

	Side by Side Plus 1	Side by Side Plus 2	Side by Side Plus 3	Side by Side Plus 4
NRS (National Reporting System) Educational Functioning Level	Low Beginning	High Beginning	Low Intermediate	High Intermediate
CASAS (Comprehensive Adult Student Assessment System)	181–190	191–200	201–210	211–220
BEST Plus (Basic English Skills Test)	401–417	418–438	439–472	473–506
BEST Oral Interview	16–28	29–41	42–50	51–57
BEST Literacy	8–35	36–46	47–53	54–65

For correlations to other major curriculum frameworks, please visit: www.pearsonlongman.com/sidebysideplus

Side by Side Plus 2 Multilevel Activity & Achievement Test Book

Copyright © 2008 by Prentice Hall Regents
Pearson Education, Inc.
All rights reserved.
No part of this publication may be reproduced, stored in a retrieval system, or transmitted in any form or by any means, electronic, mechanical, photocopying, recording, or otherwise, without the prior permission of the publisher.

Pearson Education, 10 Bank Street, White Plains, NY 10606

Editorial director: *Pam Fishman*
Vice president, director of design and production: *Rhea Banker*
Director of electronic production: *Aliza Greenblatt*
Director of manufacturing: *Patrice Fraccio*
Senior manufacturing manager: *Edith Pullman*
Director of marketing: *Oliva Fernandez*
Production editor: *Diane Cipollone*
Text design: *Wendy Wolf; TSI Graphics*
Text composition: *TSI Graphics*
Cover design: *Wanda España, Wee Design Group;*
    Warren Fischbach; Wendy Wolf
Illustrations: *Richard E. Hill*

ISBN 978-0-13-240216-3; 0-13-240216-5

Pearson Longman on the Web
Pearsonlongman.com offers online resources
for teachers and students. Access our Companion
Websites, our online catalog, and our local offices
around the world.

Visit us at **pearsonlongman.com**.

Printed in the United States of America
1 2 3 4 5 6 7 8 9 10 – BR – 13 12 11 10 09 08

CONTENTS

To the Teacher

Multilevel Grammar Worksheets ✓

Multilevel Vocabulary Worksheets ✓

Number Practice Worksheets ✓

Gazette Worksheets *yes. seperate Activiti*

Life Skills Worksheets ✓

Activity Masters

Unit Achievement Tests ✓

Learner Assessment Records *No*

Learner Progress Chart *No*

For user convenience, pages are labeled and numbered within their respective sections.

To the Teacher

Welcome to the *Side by Side Plus 2* Multilevel Activity & Achievement Test Book! This volume provides a wealth of reproducible resources for use with the *Side by Side Plus* program: unit achievement tests; assessment tools; worksheets for supplemental practice in life skills, reading, and numeracy; innovative multilevel worksheets providing grammar and vocabulary practice for students at three different ability levels; and activity masters to accompany the activity suggestions contained in the *Side by Side Plus 2* Teacher's Guide.

These materials are also available on the CD-ROM included with the Teacher's Guide. The materials may be reproduced for classroom use only in conjunction with the *Side by Side Plus* instructional program.

TESTING AND ASSESSMENT RESOURCES

UNIT ACHIEVEMENT TESTS assess student progress and prepare students for the types of standardized tests and performance assessments used by many instructional programs. The tests include multiple-choice questions that assess vocabulary, grammar, reading, and listening skills; short-answer questions that cover life skill competencies and document literacy tasks (such as reading medicine labels and filling out forms); writing assessments that can be evaluated with a standardized scoring rubric and be collected in portfolios of students' work; and speaking performance assessments designed to stimulate face-to-face interactions between students, for evaluation by the teacher using a standardized scoring rubric, or for self-evaluation by students.

Teacher support materials for the Unit Achievement Tests include a listening script, an answer key, and detailed suggestions for developing learners' test-taking strategies to promote success on standardized tests. An answer sheet is also provided to offer students useful and realistic practice "bubbling in" their answers on a separate sheet rather than in a test booklet.

LEARNER ASSESSMENT RECORDS are designed for easy scoring and documentation of student performance on the tests. The forms contain scoring rubrics for all multiple-choice questions, short-answer questions, writing assessments, and speaking assessments included on the tests. Each test is scored on a 100-point scale, providing a consistent means to evaluate student achievement of topics, vocabulary, grammar, and listening, speaking, reading, and writing skills. The Learner Assessment Records can serve as documentation of student progress during the course of the instructional program.

A LEARNER PROGRESS CHART enables students to record their test scores and chart their progress. You may want to keep the charts in a folder and have students update them as each test is completed.

WORKSHEETS

The *Side by Side Plus* worksheets are fully coordinated with units in the student book to offer valuable supplemental practice in class or at home.

LIFE SKILLS WORKSHEETS provide realia-based reading and writing activities including forms, diagrams, charts, schedules, classified ads, store directories, food labels, clothing labels, receipts, invitations, advertisements, product warning labels, medicine labels, checks, telephone directories, a calendar, a pay stub, an accident report, and a rental agreement.

MULTILEVEL GRAMMAR WORKSHEETS contain a variety of word-choice, fill-in, and sentence-completion exercises providing differentiated practice for below-level, at-level, and above-level students on each reproducible page.

MULTILEVEL VOCABULARY WORKSHEETS also offer three levels of differentiated practice through a sequence of word-choice, sentence-completion, and cloze-reading exercises on each page.

NUMBER PRACTICE WORKSHEETS develop students' numeracy skills through life-skill contexts. Topics include: basic mathematical operations (addition, subtraction, multiplication, division); elapsed time; weights and measurements; life-skill applications such as calendars, dates, money, receipts, unit pricing, advertisements, balancing a checkbook, pay stubs, floor plans, recipes, and temperatures (Fahrenheit and Celsius); and academic skills such as interpreting charts, tables, graphs, and diagrams.

GAZETTE WORKSHEETS provide practice with reading comprehension, vocabulary, and interpretation of charts and graphs, fully coordinated with the magazine-style Gazette sections in the *Side by Side Plus* student book. The bonus Gazette Audio CD that is included with the student book offers entertaining radio program-style recordings of key Gazette features. Students will enjoy listening along as they read the text and do the activities included in the Gazette worksheets. Use these resources to encourage students to extend their language-learning through self-study—building a bridge between the classroom and the home.

ACTIVITY MASTERS

ACTIVITY MASTERS include ready-to-use word cards, graphics, charts, and activity sheets for the multilevel activities and games suggested throughout the *Side by Side Plus 2* Teacher's Guide.

In conclusion, the *Side by Side Plus 2* Multilevel Activity & Achievement Test Book aims to provide you with comprehensive resources for student assessment, multilevel supplemental practice, and dynamic classroom learning through activities and games. We hope that these reproducible materials help you with your lesson-planning and enable you to offer your students an instructional program that is effective . . . responsive to students' differing needs and ability levels . . . and fun!

Steven J. Molinsky
Bill Bliss

UNIT 1
Multilevel Grammar Worksheet

Student's Name _____

Date _____

A. Choose the correct word. ★

1. I (like   like to) listen to jazz.

2. Gregory (bakes   baked) an apple pie this morning.

3. Andrea is busy. (She's working   She works) right now.

4. We (swim   swam) at the beach last Sunday afternoon.

5. I'm going to (give   gave) my wife a watch for her birthday.

6. We don't (drove   drive) to the beach very often.

B. Complete the sentences with the correct form of the verb. ★★

cook	give	go	read	write

1. Ivan _____ the newspaper now. He _____ the newspaper every day.

2. Joan _____ ten letters yesterday. She really likes to _____ letters.

3. Alan _____ dinner for his family last night, and _____ dinner for them again tonight.

4. Our son's birthday is tomorrow. We aren't going to _____ him a shirt. We _____ him a shirt last year.

5. My friends and I _____ swimming yesterday, and _____ swimming tomorrow.

C. Complete the sentences. ★★★

1. Grandma is in the yard. _____ flowers. She _____ flowers every spring.

2. _____ go to the mall today? No, I'm not. I _____ to the mall yesterday.

3. Marisa _____ her brother a book for his birthday last year. This year _____ give _____ a CD.

4. My brother isn't _____ drive to the beach today. _____ to the beach yesterday.

5. _____ make eggs for breakfast? No, I didn't. _____ them tomorrow.

Like to
Review: Simple Present,
Present Continuous, Simple Past
Future: Going to

Student's Name _____

Date _____

A. Choose the correct word. ★

1. Where's the flour? (It's   They're) on the counter.

2. We can't make pizza for lunch. There (isn't   aren't) any cheese.

3. How (much   many) meatballs do you want?

4. I want just a (little   few) rice.

5. My doctor says I eat too (much   many) eggs.

6. I don't like vegetables very much. I hardly ever eat (it   them).

7. Too (much   many) sugar (is   are) bad for your health.

B. Complete the sentences. ★★

aren't	a few	a little	How many	How much	isn't	too many

1. We can't make a salad for dinner because there _____ any lettuce.

2. Not _____ french fries, please.

3. _____ milk do you want?

4. We can't make any lemonade because there _____ any lemons.

5. I want just _____ potatoes, please.

6. _____ tomatoes did you put in the salad?

7. I bought only _____ ice cream at the supermarket.

C. Complete the sentences. Use phrases with *many, much, few,* and *little.* ★★★

1. _____ cookies did you eat?

2. Please don't give me _____ chocolate cake.

3. Do you want to have _____ more coffee?

4. _____ meat did you buy when you went to the supermarket?

5. I feel sick when I eat _____ onions.

6. Do you want some potatoes? They're delicious. Yes, please, but just _____.

A. Choose the correct word. ★

1. Please give me a (bowl   glass) of chicken soup.

2. I bought a (dozen   loaf) of bread at the supermarket.

3. Please give me (a piece   an order) of pancakes.

4. I'm going to add a (few   little) salt to the soup.

5. I ordered rice with my chicken. The rice (was   were) very tasty.

6. Please get a (bag   bottle) of ketchup when you go to the store.

7. We need a (jar   quart) of orange juice and a (bunch   head) of bananas.

B. Complete the sentences. ★★

box	bunch	cup	dish	dozen	gallon	head	piece	pound

1. We need a _____ of lettuce at the supermarket.

2. Do you want to have a _____ of hot chocolate?

3. Please buy a half _____ of Swiss cheese when you go to the store.

4. Do you want to have a _____ of apple pie for dessert?

5. Please get a _____ of cereal and a _____ eggs at the supermarket.

6. I want a _____ of ice cream for dessert.

7. We need a _____ of milk and a _____ of carrots.

C. Complete the sentences using partitives. ★★★

1. We need a _____ soup, a _____ jam, and a _____ lettuce.

2. Please give me a _____ soup and a _____ coffee.

3. Please get a _____ eggs and a half _____ cheese at the supermarket.

4. I want _____ scrambled eggs and a _____ milk, please.

5. We need two _____ whole wheat bread and a _____ flour.

6. I want a _____ ice cream, and my son wants a _____ chocolate cake.

Side by Side Plus Book 2
Unit 3 Multilevel Grammar Worksheet

Count/Non-Count Nouns
Partitives, Imperatives

© 2008 Pearson Education, Inc.
Duplication for classroom use is permitted.

UNIT 4
Multilevel Grammar Worksheet

Student's Name _____

Date _____

A. Choose the correct word. ★

1. Will your wife be here soon? Yes, she will. (I'll   She'll) be here in ten minutes.

2. Will you be ready soon? Yes, we (will   won't).

3. I'm happy. (You'll   It'll) be spring in a few weeks.

4. Our guests will be here (at   in) a little while.

5. I'm afraid I (won't   might) get sick.

6. He isn't sure. Maybe he will, and maybe he (will   won't).

7. (Will   Are) your parents return soon?

8. Be careful! Don't stand there! You (won't   might) get hurt.

9. I'm sick. (You might   I might not) go to work tomorrow.

B. Complete the sentences. ★★

1. _____ your sister get out of the hospital soon? Yes, _____.

2. Will he be home soon? Yes, _____. _____ be home in a little while.

3. Will your friends be here soon? Yes, _____. _____ be here in an hour.

4. Do you think it'll be cold tomorrow? Maybe _____, and maybe _____.

5. Rita isn't feeling well. She's afraid she _____ have the flu.

6. The train _____ arrive in a few minutes.

7. Put on your helmet! You _____ hurt your head!

8. Don't worry! You _____ get seasick!

C. Complete the following any way you wish. ★★★

1. Will _____? Yes, _____. _____ soon.

2. Do you think _____? Maybe _____, and _____.

3. Be careful! Don't _____! _____ might _____.

4. I won't _____ because I'm afraid _____.

5. Don't worry! _____ won't _____.

6. Will _____? No, _____. _____.

Side by Side Plus Book 2
Unit 4 Multilevel Grammar Worksheet

Future Tense: Will
Time Expressions, Might

© 2008 Pearson Education, Inc.
Duplication for classroom use is permitted.

UNIT 5
Multilevel Grammar Worksheet

Student's Name _____

Date _____

A. Complete the sentences with the correct form of the comparative. ★

1. Your office is (quiet) _____ than my office.

2. My new boss is (nice) _____ than my old boss.

3. My wife's computer is (powerful) _____ than my computer.

4. My next-door neighbors are (friendly) _____ than my upstairs neighbors.

5. Their dog is much (big) _____ than ours.

6. Your recipe for chocolate chip cookies is (good) _____ than mine.

7. You should hire Mr. Garcia. He's (capable) _____ than Mr. Blake.

B. Complete the sentences with the correct comparative. ★★

busy	convenient	delicious	hot	intelligent	powerful	soft

1. The weather in Miami is _____ the weather in Toronto.

2. This fan is _____ that fan.

3. I'm a mechanic. Yesterday I fixed five cars. I was even _____ today. I fixed nine cars!

4. My teacher is very smart, but I think yours is _____.

5. In my opinion, their neighborhood is _____ ours.

6. You should buy this rug. It's much _____ that rug.

7. The fish at this restaurant is okay, but the chicken is _____.

C. Complete the sentences any way you wish. Use comparatives or as _____ as. ★★★

1. My apartment _____ their apartment.

2. Airplanes _____ trains.

3. Bicycles _____ motorcycles.

4. Dogs _____ cats.

5. My _____ yours.

6. Your _____ mine.

**Comparatives, Should
Possessive Pronouns**

A. Complete the sentences with the correct form of the superlative. ★

1. My grandfather is the (kind) _____ person in our family.

2. This is the (safe) _____ car you can buy.

3. Who is the (interesting) _____ person you know?

4. Stanley is the (funny) _____ student in our class.

5. This is the (expensive) _____ television we sell.

6. Who is the (popular) _____ singer in your country?

7. In my opinion, this is the (good) _____ restaurant in the city.

B. Complete the sentences with the correct superlative. ★★

cheap	comfortable	energetic	large	noisy	polite	talented

1. Susie always says "Thank you" and "You're welcome." She's _____ little girl in the neighborhood.

2. This belt is only ten dollars. It's _____ belt in the store.

3. I like to sit in this armchair when I watch TV. It's _____ chair in our house.

4. The man upstairs plays loud music all day and all night. He's _____ neighbor in the building.

5. Sam can play three musical instruments. He's _____ person I know.

6. The house across the street has ten rooms. It's _____ house on the street.

7. Abigail jogs every morning. She's _____ person I know.

C. Complete the sentences using any superlatives you wish. ★★★

1. You should buy that hat. It's _____

2. Vote for Louise Miller. She's _____

3. I'm going to hire Ms. Chen. She's _____

4. I'm going to fire Mr. Hall. He's _____

5. Everybody likes Veronica. She's _____

6. Nobody likes Frank. He's _____

Superlatives

A. Choose the correct word. ★

1. Walk up Main Street and you'll see the bank (at   on) the right.

2. Drive (along   between) First Avenue to Tenth Street.

3. (Turn   Take) the Fifth Avenue bus.

4. Walk (up   off) Center Street and you'll see the post office on the corner.

5. Take the subway and get (on   off) at Washington Street.

6. (Stop   Walk) three blocks to Seventh Avenue.

7. (Turn   Take) left at the corner of Park Street and Second Avenue.

B. Complete the sentences with the correct word. ★★

Drive	Follow	Get off	Take	Turn	Walk up

1. _____ left and walk three blocks to Bayside Boulevard.

2. _____ at Ninth Avenue and you'll see the zoo on the right.

3. _____ the train. It's faster than the bus.

4. _____ along Oak Street and you'll see the drug store on the right.

5. _____ my directions. You won't get lost.

6. _____ Main Street to River Road and turn left.

C. Write directions to get from your school to your home. ★★★

_____

_____

_____

_____

_____

_____

_____

Imperatives

Student's Name _____

Date _____

A. Choose the correct word. ★

1. Monica is a good worker. She works very (careful   carefully).

2. Arnold goes to bed too late. He should try to go to bed (earlier   later).

3. Susan dances very well. She's very (graceful   gracefully).

4. Rick is a fast runner. He runs very (quick   fast).

5. Timothy, you need to dress more (neat   neatly).

6. If the weather (will be   is) bad tomorrow, (I   I'll) stay home and read.

7. You aren't working quickly enough. You should try to work (faster   slower).

8. If (you you'll) eat too quickly, you (shouldn't   might) get a stomachache.

9. Am I doing this (good   well) enough?

B. Complete the sentences. ★★

badly	don't	faster	good	louder	slowly	won't	you	you'll

1. Eduardo is a very _____ worker.

2. Be careful! You aren't driving _____ enough.

3. You're speaking too softly. Please speak _____.

4. Ronald isn't a good singer. He sings very _____.

5. You're typing very slowly. Please try to type _____.

6. If _____ do your homework carelessly, _____ make mistakes.

7. If you _____ study, you _____ do well on your test tomorrow.

C. Complete the sentences any way you wish. Use adverbs. ★★★

1. You should always try to _____.

2. You _____ enough. You should _____.

3. You _____ too _____. You should _____.

4. If _____, _____ will _____.

5. If _____, _____ might _____.

A. Choose the correct word. ★

1. I (was watching   watched) TV when you called.
2. Francine (lost   was losing) her purse yesterday.
3. George cut himself while he (shaved   was shaving) this morning.
4. I wasn't home at 7:00. I (washed   was washing) my clothes at the laundromat.
5. My sister went to the concert by (herself   myself) last night.
6. My wife and I got wet paint all over (yourselves   ourselves).
7. They spilled coffee all over themselves while they (were eating   ate) breakfast.
8. I saw you this morning. You (were walking   walked) out of the post office.

B. Complete the sentences. Use the past tense and the past continuous tense. ★★

call	eat	fall	play	shop	wait
drop	faint	get	read	steal	walk

1. I saw you yesterday morning at 10:00. You ___got___ off a bus.
2. I ___dropped___ my wallet while I ___was walking___ down Main Street.
3. We ___were eating___ dinner when the lights went out.
4. It was very hot, and Max ___fainted___ while he ___was waiting___ for the bus.
5. They weren't home when we ___called___ them last night.
6. I ___fell___ while I ___was playing___ tennis yesterday afternoon.
7. She was home all evening. She ___read___ a book.
8. Somebody ___stole___ our car while we ___were shopping___ at the mall.

C. Complete the sentences any way you wish. Use the past tense and the past continuous tense. ★★★

1. _____ when the lights went out.
2. I saw you this morning at 9:00. You _____.
3. I had a bad day. _____ while _____.
4. We had a bad day. _____ while _____.

A. Choose the correct word. ★

1. I (could   couldn't) finish my dinner. I was too full.

2. We (weren't   won't) able to go to the concert this afternoon.

3. I (was   wasn't) able to solve the math problem because it wasn't difficult.

4. We (won't be   weren't) able to go to the party because we had to work.

5. I've (got to   have to) pick up my cousin at the airport this afternoon.

6. Unfortunately, Julie (wasn't   won't) be able to go to the football game.

7. (You've   You) got to set up your computer today.

8. They (couldn't   weren't able) sit down on the subway this morning.

B. Complete the sentences. ★★

could	couldn't	got to	had to	was	wasn't	weren't	won't

1. Unfortunately, he _____ able to go to the picnic last weekend.

2. I'm sorry. We _____ be able to come to your party on Saturday.

3. She _____ fall asleep because she wasn't tired.

4. They couldn't go to the play because they _____ wait for the plumber.

5. We were frustrated. We _____ able to hook up our new VCR.

6. I _____ able to go swimming because the ocean wasn't too cold.

7. You've _____ study for your math test tonight.

8. I wasn't very busy, so I _____ have lunch with my co-workers today.

C. Complete the sentences any way you wish. Use *could, couldn't, able to, have to, had to,* and *have got to.* ★★★

1. _____ yesterday because _____ too _____.

2. _____ tomorrow because _____.

3. Unfortunately, _____.

4. I'm afraid I _____ because _____.

A. Choose the correct word. ★

1. You must eat more vegetables and (fewer   less) meat.

2. My doctor told me to eat (fewer   less) rich desserts.

3. I'm a little too heavy. I (mustn't   must) lose some weight.

4. My cake was terrible. I used (fewer   less) flour than the recipe called for.

5. I don't have to stop eating candy, but I (must   mustn't) have it very often.

6. I'm concerned about your knees. You (shouldn't   must) stop jogging every day.

7. If you have a bad cold, you (should   mustn't) drink some hot tea. It will help.

8. I have high blood pressure. I (must   mustn't) relax more often.

B. Complete the sentences. ★★

don't have to	fewer	have to	less	must	mustn't	should

1. Do I _____ stop eating french fries?

2. My doctor says I must eat _____ eggs and more yogurt.

3. You must eat _____ rice and more vegetables.

4. I have a bad cold. What _____ I do? Do you have any advice?

5. Mr. Martinez. I'm concerned about your blood pressure. You _____ lose some weight.

6. I _____ stop eating candy, but I _____ eat a lot of it.

C. You went to the doctor for a checkup. What advice did your doctor give you? Use *fewer, less, more, must, mustn't,* and *don't have to.* ★★★

1. You _____.

2. You _____.

3. You _____.

4. You _____.

5. You _____.

A. Choose the correct word. ★

1. I won't be home this evening. I'll (shop   be shopping) at the supermarket.

2. My wife and I (we'll   will be) visiting our relatives in Chicago this weekend.

3. I won't come over now. I don't want to disturb you. (You'll   I'll) be ironing.

4. Alice will be busy today. (She's going   She'll) be cleaning her garage.

5. They'll be staying in San Francisco (for   until) a week.

6. I'll be studying tonight (for   until) 10:00 P.M.

7. We'll be arriving in Miami (until   at) 11:45 A.M.

8. (I'll   I'll be) see you later.

B. Complete the sentences. Use the future continuous tense. ★★

arrive	iron	practice	shop
get	pay	rearrange	stay

at	for	until

1. I'll be busy tomorrow morning. _____ my shirts.

2. Mr. and Mrs. Jenkins will be home all evening. _____ bills.

3. My wife and I _____ our furniture this afternoon.

4. My husband and I _____ at this supermarket this morning.

5. Grandpa is feeling better. _____ out of the hospital in a few days.

6. The train _____ in New York _____ 7:17 P.M.

7. My daughter _____ the violin _____ a few more minutes.

8. Our relatives from Detroit _____ with us _____ next weekend.

C. Complete the sentences any way you wish. Use the future continuous tense. ★★★

1. _____ all afternoon.

2. _____ until Sunday.

3. _____ at 9:00 P.M.

4. _____ for a few more hours.

Side by Side Plus Book 2
Unit 12 Multilevel Grammar Worksheet

Future Continuous Tense
Time Expressions

© 2008 Pearson Education, Inc.
Duplication for classroom use is permitted.

A. Choose the correct word. ★

1. Look at Grandpa! He's raking the leaves by (himself   herself).

2. Charlie, please be careful! You might hurt (yourself   yourselves).

3. This isn't my briefcase. It's (your   yours). (My   Mine) is larger.

4. I couldn't fall asleep because my neighbors (played   were playing) loud music.

5. The mechanic (was charging   charged) us a lot of money to fix our car.

6. I can't help you. I don't know (something   anything) about computers.

7. I won't be home this afternoon. (I'll shop   I'll be shopping) at the mall.

8. (Somebody   Anybody) from the insurance company is on the phone.

B. Complete the sentences. ★★

anything	himself	myself	something	were vacuuming
hers	mine	our	vacuumed	yourself

1. You should make your lunch by _____, and I'll make my lunch by _____.

2. My wife and I lost our cell phones. I can't find _____, and she can't find

   _____.

3. My husband can't fix his camera by _____. He doesn't know _____
   about cameras.

4. We need to call a repairperson. _____ is wrong with _____ dishwasher.

5. I couldn't fall asleep because my upstairs neighbors _____ their rugs.

   They _____ them until 4:30 A.M.

C. Complete the sentences any way you wish. ★★★

1. That's okay. _____ can _____ by _____.

2. This isn't _____, but it might be _____. _____ yesterday.

3. I couldn't fall asleep because _____ until _____.

4. I don't know _____ about _____, but I'm sure _____.

Some/Any, Pronoun Review
Verb Tense Review

Side by Side Plus 2
Multilevel Grammar Worksheets Answer Key

UNIT 1

A.
1. like to
2. baked
3. She's working
4. swam
5. give
6. drive

B.
1. is reading, reads
2. wrote, write
3. cooked, he's going to cook
4. give, gave
5. went, we're going to go

C.
1. She's planting, plants
2. Are you going to, went
3. gave, she's going to, him
4. going to, He drove
5. Did you, I'm going to make

UNIT 2

A.
1. It's
2. isn't
3. many
4. little
5. many
6. them
7. much, is

B.
1. isn't
2. too many
3. How much
4. aren't
5. a few
6. How many
7. a little

C.
1. How many
2. too much
3. a little
4. How much
5. too many
6. a few

UNIT 3

A.
1. bowl
2. loaf
3. an order
4. little
5. was
6. bottle
7. quart, bunch

B.
1. head
2. cup
3. pound
4. piece
5. box, dozen
6. dish
7. gallon, bunch

C.
1. can of, jar of, head of
2. bowl of, cup of
3. dozen, pound of
4. an order of, glass of
5. loaves of, bag of
6. dish of, piece of

UNIT 4

A.
1. She'll
2. will
3. It'll
4. in
5. might
6. won't
7. Will
8. might
9. I might not

B.
1. Will, she will
2. he will, He'll
3. they will, They'll
4. it will, it won't
5. might
6. will
7. might
8. won't

C.
(Answers will vary.)

UNIT 5

A.
1. quieter
2. nicer
3. more powerful
4. friendlier
5. bigger
6. better
7. more capable

B.
1. hotter than
2. more powerful
3. busier
4. more intelligent
5. more convenient than
6. softer than
7. more delicious

C.
(Answers will vary.)

UNIT 6

A.
1. kindest
2. safest
3. most interesting
4. funniest
5. most expensive
6. most popular
7. best

B.
1. the most polite
2. the cheapest
3. the most comfortable
4. the noisiest
5. the most talented
6. the largest
7. the most energetic

C.
(Answers will vary.)

UNIT 7

A.
1. on
2. along
3. Take
4. up
5. off
6. Walk
7. Turn

B.
1. Turn
2. Get off
3. Take
4. Drive
5. Follow
6. Walk up

C.
(Directions will vary.)

UNIT 8

A.
1. carefully
2. earlier
3. graceful
4. fast
5. neatly
6. is, I'll
7. faster
8. you, might
9. well

B.
1. good
2. slowly
3. louder
4. badly
5. faster
6. you, you'll
7. don't, won't

C.
(Answers will vary.)

UNIT 9

A.
1. was watching
2. lost
3. was shaving
4. was washing
5. herself
6. ourselves
7. were eating
8. were walking

B.
1. were getting
2. dropped,
   was walking
3. were eating
4. fainted,
   was waiting
5. called
6. fell,
   was playing
7. was reading
8. stole,
   were shopping

C.
(Answers will vary.)

UNIT 10

A.
1. couldn't
2. weren't
3. was
4. weren't
5. got to
6. won't
7. You've
8. couldn't

B.
1. wasn't
2. won't
3. couldn't
4. had to
5. weren't
6. was
7. got to
8. could

C.
(Answers will vary.)

UNIT 11

A.
1. less
2. fewer
3. must
4. less
5. mustn't
6. must
7. should
8. must

B.
1. have to
2. fewer
3. less
4. should
5. must
6. don't have to, mustn't

C.
(Answers will vary.)

UNIT 12

A.
1. be shopping
2. will be
3. You'll
4. She'll
5. for
6. until
7. at
8. I'll

B.
1. I'll be ironing
2. They'll be paying
3. will be rearranging
4. will be shopping
5. He'll be getting
6. will be arriving, at
7. will be practicing, for
8. will be staying, until

C.
(Answers will vary.)

UNIT 13

A.
1. himself
2. yourself
3. yours, Mine
4. were playing
5. charged
6. anything
7. I'll be shopping
8. Somebody

B.
1. yourself, myself
2. mine, hers
3. himself, anything
4. Something, our
5. were vacuuming, vacuumed

C.
(Answers will vary.)

A. Choose the correct word. ★

1. How (age   old) is your daughter?

2. There are exercise (classes   concerts) every Friday at the Community Center.

3. Last weekend we went to Mount Snow on a hiking (dance   trip).

4. The school is (celebrating   making) Martin Luther King, Jr. Day on Monday.

5. My daughter is eight years old. She goes to (pre-school   elementary school).

6. After high school, my son is going to go to (graduate school   college).

7. My date of (birth   birthday) is October 7, 1990.

8. I want to (register   attend) my son for school.

B. Complete the sentences. ★★

concert   date   free   grade   medical   private

1. My son is in the fifth _____.

2. Lisa Martini is giving a jazz _____ tonight.

3. We're paying for our fifteen-year-old son to attend a _____ school.

4. Public schools are _____.

5. Marie is going to be a doctor. Right now she's studying in _____ school.

6. What's your daughter's _____ of birth?

C. Write the correct words to complete the conversation. ★★★

A. May I _____[1] you?

B. Yes, please. I want to _____[2] my daughter for school.

A. Okay. What's her last _____[3]?

B. Wong.

A. And her _____[4] name?

B. Amelia.

A. What's her date of _____[5]?

B. July 23, 2005.

UNIT 2
Multilevel Vocabulary Worksheet

Student's Name _____
Date _____

A. Choose the correct word. ★

1. The P.E. teacher's classes are in the (auditorium   gym).

2. There's a lunchroom monitor in the (cafeteria   library).

3. The guidance (counselor   worker) helps students make good decisions.

4. The school (secretary   officer) works in the school office.

5. Connect the power (keyboard   cable) to the port.

6. The power (button   mouse) is on the front of the computer.

7. To use the Internet, connect the computer to (an outlet   a modem).

B. Complete the sentences. ★★

cafeteria	keyboard	lab	office	port	surge protector

1. When I feel sick at school, I go to the nurse's _____.

2. The _____ workers serve lunch every day.

3. The computer _____ is on the second floor.

4. Connect this cable to the _____ on the back of the computer.

5. Connect the cable on your _____ to a USB port.

6. Always plug your computer into an outlet with a _____.

C. Write the correct words to complete the paragraph. ★★★

Many people work in a school. The _____[1] manages the

school. The school _____[2] works in the front office and answers the

phone and helps the principal. The _____[3] takes care of the library.

The school _____[4] takes care of children when they're sick. The

_____[5] teach the classes. The cafeteria _____[6] prepare

and serve the food. And the _____[7] makes sure everyone is safe.

Multilevel Vocabulary Worksheet

Student's Name _____

Date _____

A. Choose the correct word. ★

1. How much is a (loaf   jar) of bread?

2. How much does a (gallon   bag) of milk cost?

3. How much is a (box   bunch) of bananas?

4. How much does a (bowl   piece) of soup cost?

5. Apples are in the (Dairy   Produce) section.

6. Ice cream is in the (Beverages   Frozen Foods) section.

7. Juice is in the (Beverages   Baked Goods) section.

8. Chicken is in the (Meat   Dairy) section.

B. Complete the sentences. ★★

bottle	bread	cheese	dozen	lettuce	pound

1. _____ is in the Produce section.

2. _____ is in the Baked Goods section.

3. _____ is in the Dairy section.

4. How much does a _____ eggs cost?

5. How much is a _____ of fish?

6. How much is a _____ of soda?

C. Write the correct words to complete the conversation. ★★★

A. _____[1] me. Where are the tomatoes?

B. They're in the _____[2] section.

A. And _____[3] is the milk?

B. It's in the _____[4] section.

A. Okay. And how much does this _____[5] of lettuce cost?

B. $2.59.

A. Thank you.

A. Choose the correct word. ★

1. How many (guests   hosts) did you invite to the party?

2. We're (requesting   celebrating) our anniversary this weekend.

3. We're planning a surprise (wedding   party) for Susan Murphy.

4. Would you like to go out for (lunch   work) today?

5. Our wedding (presence   reception) was at the Pine Tree Inn.

6. It's (impolite   polite) to say *please* and *thank you.*

7. Maria and Luis are getting (married   invited) in a church.

B. Complete the sentences. ★★

dinner	guests	honor	hosts	invitations	punctuality	RSVP

1. The Johnsons have great parties. They're wonderful _____.

2. It's going to be a big wedding. There will be more than 250 _____.

3. _____ before September 30th by e-mail or by phone.

4. Would you like to go out for _____ with me this evening?

5. We request the _____ of your presence at our daughter's wedding.

6. Cindy sent over 100 _____ to her holiday party this year.

7. I'm going to arrive on time because _____ is important.

C. Write the correct words to complete the invitation. ★★★

It's a Surprise _____[1]!

Please join us to _____[2] Sam Wong's 70th _____[3].

Saturday July 14th at the Garden Club.

Be there at 6:00. Don't be _____[4]!

_____[5] before June 30th.

UNIT 5
Multilevel Vocabulary Worksheet

Student's Name _____

Date _____

A. Choose the correct word. ★

1. Which air conditioner do you (compare   recommend)?

2. I like this TV because the screen is (wider   heavier).

3. This car is faster and more (delicious   powerful) than our old one.

4. This mattress is more (comfortable   interesting) than that one.

5. Small cars are more (hospitable   efficient) than big cars.

6. This watch is more (fashionable   talented) that that one.

7. Everything costs more, so the workers want (higher   lower) pay.

8. This neighborhood is more (convenient   sympathetic) because it's close to stores and restaurants.

B. Complete the sentences. ★★

cheaper	easier-to-use	faster	larger	lighter	quieter	safer

1. I like the new laptop computers. They're _____ than the old heavy ones.

2. This refrigerator costs less. It's _____ than that one.

3. This printer is very slow. I want a _____ one.

4. Our car is too small. We need a _____ one.

5. Their dishwasher is very noisy. They need a _____ one.

6. This heavy car isn't as efficient, but it's _____ in accidents.

7. I like my old cell phone because it's _____ than the new fancy ones.

C. Write the correct words to complete the paragraph. ★★★

Riverdale is a different town than it was ten years ago. The streets aren't dirty any more. They're very _____[1]. The buses aren't noisy now. They're _____[2]. The trains come on time. They're very _____[3]. The parks aren't dangerous. They're _____[4] now. The downtown isn't dull and boring. It's very _____[5]. But unfortunately, the taxes aren't low any more. They're _____[6].

UNIT 6
Multilevel Vocabulary Worksheet

Student's Name _____

Date _____

A. Choose the correct word. ★

1. DVD players are in the (Furniture   Electronics) department.
2. Dishes and cups are in the (Housewares   Household Appliances) department.
3. I'm going to deposit this in our (balance   checking) account.
4. How much is this sweater? It doesn't have a (price tag   refund).
5. This fan doesn't work. I think it's (defective   attached).
6. Can I pay with a (withdrawal   check)?
7. I'm sorry. You can't return this. It was a (final   credit) sale.

B. Complete the sentences. ★★

accept	enter	insert	move	purchase	receive

1. To use an ATM, you have to _____ your card into the machine.
2. _____ your PIN on the keypad.
3. I'm sorry. We don't _____ returns on underwear or swimwear.
4. If you have your receipt, you can _____ a store credit.
5. I want to _____ money from one account to another.
6. The price of the item and the date of _____ are on the receipt.

C. Write the correct words to complete the conversation. ★★★

A. I'd like to _____[1] these shoes.

B. What's the _____[2] with them?

A. They're _____[3] tight.

B. Would you like to _____[4] them? We have many different kinds of shoes in our shoe department.

A. No, thank you. I'd like a _____[5], please.

B. Okay. Do you have your _____[6]?

A. Yes. Here it is.

A. Choose the correct word. ★

1. How many (times   hours) does the post office pick up the mail on the weekend?

2. Accidents can happen when (cars   passengers) are in bad condition.

3. Be careful! There's a (pedestrian   traffic) crosswalk ahead!

4. Slow down! The (license   speed limit) is 45 miles an hour.

5. Keep the (windshield   brakes) clean so you can see while you drive.

6. The driver always sits in the (front   back) seat.

7. When it rains, the road gets (sleepy   slippery).

B. Complete the sentences. ★★

detour	headlights	lanes	registration	seat	windshield wipers

1. Children under five should always ride in a child safety _____.

2. Turn on your _____ in the fog and at night.

3. Turn on your _____ in the rain.

4. Look before you change _____ on the highway.

5. If you're in an accident, the police will want to see your license,

   _____, and insurance card.

6. The road is closed. We have to take a _____.

C. Write the correct words to complete the paragraph. ★★★

Driving Safety

Always wear your _____[1] when you drive. Also, make sure all the

_____[2] in the car are also wearing one. Pay attention to traffic signs,

_____[3] conditions, and other drivers. _____[4] down

when you see a school safety sign. Stop when you see someone walking across a

_____[5]. Don't drive too fast, and follow the speed _____[6],

even when it's 15 miles an hour.

UNIT 8
Multilevel Vocabulary Worksheet

Student's Name _____

Date _____

A. Choose the correct word. ★

1. The job is for 40 hours a week. It's a (full-time   part-time) job.

2. We're looking for someone with two years (resume   experience).

3. I fell at work. I need to submit an accident (report   application).

4. Could I possibly take a (break   position)? The reason is I don't feel well.

5. Last week I worked 45 hours, so I got five hours (overtime   regular) pay.

6. After deductions, my (gross   net) pay is $125 a week.

7. To be a driver, you need to have an excellent driving (diploma   record).

8. I have good (skills   benefits). I get four weeks vacation and good health insurance.

B. Complete the sentences. ★★

apply	come	complete	earn	pay	send	train

1. No experience is necessary. The supervisor will _____ you.

2. As an electrician, you'll _____ a salary of $600 a week.

3. Please _____ two copies of your resume to this address.

4. Could I possibly _____ in late tomorrow morning? I have a parent-teacher conference.

5. I have to _____ in person for this job.

6. Look at your pay stub. You can see how much you _____ in taxes.

7. You need to _____ this report and give it to your supervisor.

C. Write the correct words to complete the paragraph. ★★★

Amy is a very capable person. First she was a secretary, so she has good computer

_____[1]. Then she worked as a waitress, so she can _____[2]

orders and _____[3] customers. Then she became a cook, so she can

_____[4] salads and cook many dishes. Then she was a restaurant supervisor,

so she can _____[5] employees. Maybe Amy will open her own restaurant

some day!

Side by Side Plus Book 2
Unit 8 Multilevel Vocabulary Worksheet

© 2008 Pearson Education, Inc.
Duplication for classroom use is permitted.

UNIT 9
Multilevel Vocabulary Worksheet

Student's Name _____

Date _____

A. Choose the correct word. ★

1. You need an (evacuation   electrical) plan in case of a hurricane.

2. You should (find   cover) your head during an earthquake.

3. If you get a bee (sting   burn), apply ice.

4. If someone is (choking   bleeding), tell the person to cough.

5. I think my (daughter   first-aid kit) overdosed on some medicine.

6. To report an emergency, (teach   dial) 911.

7. Some household products are (sterile   harmful) if swallowed.

8. Help! There's a man with a (gun   stinger) in my store!

B. Complete the sentences. ★★

attention	burn	doorway	medicine	poison	shock	wound

1. If someone gets an electric _____, turn off the power.

2. If a dog bites you, wash the _____ with soap and water for five minutes.

3. If you get a _____, put it in cool water for five minutes.

4. If a person can't breathe, get medical _____ immediately.

5. If there's an earthquake, get down on your knees under a table or _____.

6. To be ready for an emergency evacuation, have a kit with _____, flashlights, batteries, food, and water.

7. If someone drinks a household product, call the _____ Control Center immediately.

C. Write the correct words to complete the paragraph. ★★★

Home Safety

Keep a fire _____[1] in the kitchen. Change the batteries in your smoke

_____[2] twice a year. Keep a first-aid _____[3] in a convenient

place. Keep household products out of _____[4] of children. Keep a list of

_____[5] phone numbers close to your telephone.

Student's Name _____

Date _____

A. Choose the correct word. ★

1. My kitchen (sink   light) is clogged.

2. If you want to rent the apartment, call the (landlord   tenant).

3. The apartment has one and a half (kitchens   bathrooms).

4. There's a laundry room in the (basement   driveway).

5. Heat, electricity, and cable aren't (allowed   included) in the rent.

6. All residents must read the building rules and (regulations   plans).

7. Don't make noise that (disturbs   disconnects) people in the building.

B. Complete the sentences. ★★

balcony	dishwasher	order	satellite	storage	superintendent

1. If you have a problem with your apartment, call the _____.

2. Don't use barbecue grills on your _____.

3. Talk to the building manager before you install a _____ dish.

4. You can pay the rent with a check or money _____.

5. The _____ in my apartment is leaking.

6. Keep bicycles and other items in the _____ room in the basement.

C. Write the correct words to complete the conversation. ★★★

A. How much is the _____[1] for the two-bedroom apartment?

B. It's $925 a _____[2].

A. Does that include _____[3]?

B. No. Gas and electricity are not included.

A. Is there a security _____[4]?

B. Yes. We require one month's rent.

A. Are _____[5] allowed?

B. Cats and small dogs are allowed, but no large animals. And _____[6] is included in the rent. There's a space for one car.

A. Choose the correct word. ★

1. Your (doctor   pharmacist) will write a prescription for your medicine.

2. Take one (capsule   syrup) every four hours.

3. Throw away your medicine if it's past the (decongestant   expiration) date.

4. Whole wheat bread and brown rice are whole (grains   minerals).

5. (Fat   Protein) from meat, butter, and fried foods is bad for your heart.

6. I have a stiff (head   neck).

7. My son will be (sick   absent) from school today.

8. I have a great (recipe   remedy) for vegetable soup.

9. I'd like to make an (appointment   ailment) with the doctor.

B. Complete the sentences. ★★

| dosage | effects | energy | ingredients | nutrients | reliever |

1. Read the medicine label to make sure you take the right _____.

2. This is a complicated recipe. It has a lot of _____.

3. Which pain _____ do you recommend for a headache?

4. Vitamins, minerals, and protein are _____.

5. This medicine has some possible side _____, including stomach upset and drowsiness.

6. It's important to eat healthy foods. They give you _____.

C. Write the correct words to complete the conversation. ★★★

A. Hello. This is Amy Chan. I'm _____[1], but I can't come to work today.

I'm _____[2].

B. Oh. What's the _____[3]?

A. I have a fever and a sore _____[4].

B. I'm sorry to _____[5] that. I _____[6] you feel better _____[7].

Student's Name _____

Date _____

A. Choose the correct word. ★

1. Amanda isn't here. Can I (tell   take) a message?

2. Sorry. There's nobody here (named   dialed) Victor.

3. You can find your friend's telephone number in the (Yellow   White) Pages.

4. I apologize. I dialed the (right   wrong) number.

5. Look up the Building Inspector's number in the (White   Government) Pages.

6. I'm going to call the Board of Health to complain about that (restaurant   dog).

7. You can add your name to our company mailing (message   list).

8. This is an automated response system. (Press   Place) 9 to locate a Rite-Way store near you.

B. Complete the sentences. ★★

account	department	directory	school	service	system

1. I want to register my 12-year-old son for middle _____.

2. There's a problem with my order. I need to call customer _____.

3. A traffic light on our street is broken. We should call the highway _____.

4. Do you have a telephone _____? I need to look in the Yellow Pages.

5. I have a question about my credit card _____. I think there's a mistake on my bill.

6. Nobody answers the phone anymore! Most companies now use an automated response _____.

C. Write the correct words to complete the conversation. ★★★

A. Hello. _____[1] is Pam Sanders. May I _____[2] with Pedro?

B. Just a _____[3]. . . . I'm sorry. He isn't _____[4] right now. Can I take a _____[5]?

A. Yes. Please _____[6] him that Pam called.

A. Choose the correct word. ★

1. We have a problem in our apartment. The toilet doesn't (drip   flush) properly.

2. The lock on our front door is broken. The key gets (stuck   clogged).

3. There's a problem with my window. I'm going to (request   report) a repair.

4. Every apartment must have an emergency (detector   exit).

5. If I pay my rent late, I have to pay a late (deposit   fee).

6. The plumbing, heat, and electricity must be in working (condition   enforcement).

7. A tenant can pay for a repair and (evict   deduct) the cost from the rent bill.

8. The landlord must (repair   require) all appliances that come with the apartment.

9. There is a security (deposit   lock) of $900. I'll get it back if I keep the apartment in good condition.

B. Complete the sentences. ★★

agreement	department	form	maintenance	responsibility	right

1. Every tenant has the _____ to a safe and healthy apartment.

2. The tenant's _____ is to take good care of the apartment.

3. I need a _____ person to check my toilet. It keeps running.

4. If you need a repair, you can call our office or fill out a request _____.

5. The tenant and the landlord must read and sign a rental _____.

6. Call the health _____ if your landlord won't make important repairs.

C. Write the correct words to complete the conversation. ★★★

A. I called a few days ago. My stove is _____[1].

B. I'm _____[2]. Please tell me the _____[3] again.

A. One _____[4] doesn't light, and I can smell gas. I think the gas is _____[5].

B. Okay. I'll make sure someone _____[6] your stove right away.

Side by Side Plus 2
Multilevel Vocabulary Worksheets Answer Key

UNIT 1

A.
1. old
2. classes
3. trip
4. celebrating
5. elementary school
6. college
7. birth
8. register

B.
1. grade
2. concert
3. private
4. free
5. medical
6. date

C.
1. help
2. register
3. name
4. birth
5. first

UNIT 2

A.
1. gym
2. cafeteria
3. counselor
4. secretary
5. cable
6. button
7. a modem

B.
1. office
2. cafeteria
3. lab
4. port
5. keyboard
6. surge protector

C.
1. principal
2. secretary
3. librarian
4. nurse
5. teachers
6. workers
7. security officer

UNIT 3

A.
1. loaf
2. gallon
3. bunch
4. bowl
5. Produce
6. Frozen Foods
7. Beverages
8. Meat

B.
1. Lettuce
2. Bread
3. Cheese
4. dozen
5. pound
6. bottle

C.
1. Excuse
2. Produce
3. where
4. Dairy
5. head

UNIT 4

A.
1. guests
2. celebrating
3. party
4. lunch
5. reception
6. polite
7. married

B.
1. hosts
2. guests
3. RSVP
4. dinner
5. honor
6. invitations
7. punctuality

C.
1. Party
2. celebrate
3. birthday
4. late
5. RSVP

UNIT 5

A.
1. recommend
2. wider
3. powerful
4. comfortable
5. efficient
6. fashionable
7. higher
8. convenient

B.
1. lighter
2. cheaper
3. faster
4. larger
5. quieter
6. safer
7. easier-to-use

C.
1. clean
2. quiet
3. reliable
4. safe
5. interesting/exciting
6. high

UNIT 6

A.
1. Electronics
2. Housewares
3. checking
4. price tag
5. defective
6. check
7. final

B.
1. insert
2. Enter
3. accept
4. receive
5. move
6. purchase

C.
1. return
2. matter
3. too
4. exchange
5. refund
6. receipt

UNIT 7

A.
1. times
2. cars
3. pedestrian
4. speed limit
5. windshield
6. front
7. slippery

B.
1. seat
2. headlights
3. windshield wipers
4. lanes
5. registration
6. detour

C.
1. seat belt
2. passengers
3. road
4. Slow
5. crosswalk
6. limit

UNIT 8

A.
1. full-time
2. experience
3. report
4. break
5. overtime
6. net
7. record
8. benefits

B.
1. train
2. earn
3. send
4. come
5. apply
6. pay
7. complete

C.
1. skills
2. take
3. serve
4. prepare/make
5. supervise

UNIT 9

A.
1. evacuation
2. cover
3. sting
4. choking
5. daughter
6. dial
7. harmful
8. gun

B.
1. shock
2. wound
3. burn
4. attention
5. doorway
6. medicine
7. Poison

C.
1. extinguisher
2. detector
3. kit
4. reach
5. emergency

UNIT 10

A.
1. sink
2. landlord
3. bathrooms
4. basement
5. included
6. regulations
7. disturbs

B.
1. superintendent
2. balcony
3. satellite
4. order
5. dishwasher
6. storage

C.
1. rent
2. month
3. utilities
4. deposit
5. pets
6. parking

UNIT 11

A.
1. doctor
2. capsule
3. expiration
4. grains
5. Fat
6. neck
7. absent
8. recipe
9. appointment

B.
1. dosage
2. ingredients
3. reliever
4. nutrients
5. effects
6. energy

C.
1. sorry
2. sick
3. matter
4. throat
5. hear
6. hope
7. soon

UNIT 12

A.
1. take
2. named
3. White
4. wrong
5. Government
6. restaurant
7. list
8. Press

B.
1. school
2. service
3. department
4. directory
5. account
6. system

C.
1. This
2. speak
3. moment
4. here
5. message
6. tell

UNIT 13

A.
1. flush
2. stuck
3. request
4. exit
5. fee
6. condition
7. deduct
8. repair
9. deposit

B.
1. right
2. responsibility
3. maintenance
4. form
5. agreement
6. department

C.
1. broken
2. sorry
3. problem
4. burner
5. leaking
6. fixes/repairs

Student's Name _____

Date _____

Word Problems with Calendars, Dates, & Ordinal Numbers

Look at the calendar.   Write the correct dates.

June 2008						
Sunday	Monday	Tuesday	Wednesday	Thursday	Friday	Saturday
		1	2	3	4	5 Grandparents' 50th anniversary
6	7	8	9	10 Ana's 20th birthday!	11	12
13	14 Uncle Sam's 40th birthday!	15	16	17	18 Aunt Clara's 48th birthday!	19
20 Parkers' 25th anniversary	21	22	23 Michael's 12th birthday!	24	25	26
27	28	29	30			

1. What is the first Monday of the month?   Monday, June _____

2. What is the second Tuesday of the month?   Tuesday, June _____

3. What is the third Thursday of the month?   Thursday, June _____

4. What is the fifth Wednesday of the month?   Wednesday, June _____

5. What is Ana's date of birth? (month/day/year)   __ __ / __ __ / __ __ __ __

6. What is Uncle Sam's date of birth?   __ __ / __ __ / __ __ __ __

7. What is Michael's date of birth?   __ __ / __ __ / __ __ __ __

8. What is Aunt Clara's date of birth?   __ __ / __ __ / __ __ __ __

9. What is the Parkers' wedding date?   __ __ / __ __ / __ __ __ __

10. What is the grandparents' wedding date?   __ __ / __ __ / __ __ __ __

Student's Name _____

Date _____

Word Problems with Elapsed Time

Look at Laura's school schedule and answer the questions.

	Monday	Tuesday	Wednesday	Thursday	Friday
Period 1 8:00 – 8:45	English	English	English	English	English
Period 2 9:00 – 9:45	Science	Science	Science	Science	Science
Period 3 10:00 – 10:45	Math	Math	Math	Math	Math
Period 4 11:00 – 11:45	Library	P.E.	Computer Lab	P.E.	Computer Lab
11:45 – 12:15	LUNCH	LUNCH	LUNCH	LUNCH	LUNCH
Period 5 12:15 – 1:00	Spanish	Spanish	Spanish	Spanish	Music
Period 6 1:15 – 2:00	History	History	History	History	History

1. How much time does Laura have for lunch every day? _____ minutes

2. How long is Laura's school day? _____ hours

3. How much time does Laura spend in Spanish class each week? _____ hours

4. How much time does Laura spend in Science class each week?

    _____ hours and _____ minutes

5. How much more time does Laura spend in History class than in Music class each week? _____ hours

6. How much more time does Laura spend in the computer lab than in the library each week? _____ minutes

7. How much more time does Laura spend in English class than in P.E. each week? _____ hours and _____ minutes

Money, Receipts, & Unit Pricing

A. Look at the receipts and answer the questions.

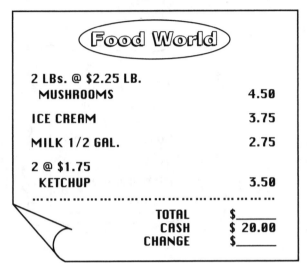

```
          Food World

2 LBs. @ $2.25 LB.
  MUSHROOMS               4.50
ICE CREAM                 3.75
MILK 1/2 GAL.             2.75
2 @ $1.75
  KETCHUP                 3.50
......................................
             TOTAL      $_____
             CASH       $ 20.00
             CHANGE     $_____
```

```
          Moon's Market

BAGGED CARROTS            1.75
GREEN BEANS
  2.5 LBS. @ $2.00/LB.    5.00
GRAPES
  2 LBS. @ $1.19/LB       2.38
LETTUCE
  2 @ $1.75/HEAD          3.50
BANANAS
  3 LBS @ $.50/LB         1.50
......................................
             TOTAL      $ 14.13
             CASH       $ 15.00
             CHANGE     $   .87
```

1. How much is the total? _____

2. How much is the change? _____

3. How much did he spend on fruit? _____

4. How much did he spend on vegetables? _____

B. Look at the supermarket advertisements. Check the store with the lower price.

GREEN'S GROCERIES

Crunch Breakfast Cereal
Buy one, get one free. (regular price $2.99)

Belle Farm Bread $3.00/loaf

Green's Orange Juice 1 quart
2 for $4.00

Granny's Chicken Soup
$1.50 a can

Simply Soda
4 cans for $1

~RAY'S~

Crunch Breakfast Cereal $1.99 each

Belle Farm Bread Buy 2, get one free.
(regular price $3.50)

Orange Juice 1 quart $2.50

Ray's Chicken Soup 4 cans for $5

Drink Up Soda 40 cents a can

		Green's	Ray's			Green's	Ray's
1.	One box of breakfast cereal	☐	✔	4.	One quart of orange juice	☐	☐
2.	Two boxes of breakfast cereal	☐	☐	5.	One can of soda	☐	☐
3.	Three loaves of Belle Farm Bread	☐	☐	6.	One can of chicken soup	☐	☐

Word Problems with Elapsed Time

Read the invitation and the housing ad. Solve the word problems.

1. The Sterns arrived at the Lees' party at 6:15. How early were they?
   a. 10 minutes early
   b. 15 minutes early
   c. 20 minutes early

2. The Watsons arrived at the Lees' party at 7:10. How late were they?
   a. 20 minutes late
   b. 35 minutes late
   c. 40 minutes late

3. Stella arrived at the Lees' party at 6:45 and stayed until 11:25. How long did she stay?
   a. 4 hours and 40 minutes
   b. 5 hours and 35 minutes
   c. 5 hours and 40 minutes

4. The first guests arrived at the Lees' party at 6:15 and the last guest left at 11:25. How long was their party?
   a. 4 hours and 55 minutes
   b. 5 hours and 10 minutes
   c. 5 hours and 25 minutes

5. How long is the open house?
   a. 2 hours and 30 minutes
   b. 3 hours
   c. 3 hours and 30 minutes

6. The rental agent arrived at 10:15 and worked until the end of the open house. How many hours did she work?
   a. 3 hours and 15 minutes
   b. 3 hours and 45 minutes
   c. 4 hours and 15 minutes

7. Sam Johnson visited the open house. He stayed from 12:35 to 1:10. How long did he stay?
   a. 25 minutes
   b. 35 minutes
   c. 45 minutes

8. The agent wrote down the name of each visitor and the time when each visitor came and left. Which visitor stayed the longest?
   a. Chuck Owen: 11:05 – 11:50
   b. Sam Johnson: 12:35 – 1:10
   c. Evan Wilson: 12:45 – 1:20.

Student's Name _____

Date _____

Word Problems with Comparatives

A. Look at the refrigerator information stickers and solve the word problems.

Refrigerator Model 2000
61 inches high   29 1/2 inches wide
29 1/2 inches deep
▼
Energy cost per year: $78
Price: $847

Refrigerator Model 3010
64 1/2 inches high   35 1/2 inches wide
32 inches deep
▼
Energy cost per year: $51
Price: $999

1. How much higher is Model 3010 than Model 2000?
   a. 2 1/2 inches   c. 3 1/2 inches
   b. 3 inches   d. 4 1/2 inches

2. How much wider is Model 3010 than Model 2000?
   a. 5 1/2 inches   c. 6 1/2 inches
   b. 6 inches   d. 7 inches

3. How much deeper is Model 3010 than Model 2000?
   a. 2 1/2 inches   c. 3 1/2 inches
   b. 3 inches   d. 4 inches

4. How much more expensive is Model 3010 to buy?
   a. $52   c. $142
   b. $133   d. $152

5. How much more expensive is Model 2000 to use each year?
   a. $27   c. $92
   b. $47   d. $152

6. How much more expensive is Model 2000 to buy and use for 10 years?
   a. $68   c. $152
   b. $118   d. $270

B. Solve the word problems.

1. Jim is buying a laptop computer. One model weighs 4 1/2 pounds. The other model weighs 7 pounds. What is their difference in weight?
   a. 1 1/2 pounds
   b. 2 1/2 pounds
   c. 3 1/2 pounds

2. Linda is buying a printer. One printer costs $149.50 and the other costs $185. What is the difference in cost?
   a. $35.50
   b. $40.50
   c. $45.50

3. Paul has a new couch. It's 91 inches wide and 38 inches high. His old couch was 77 inches wide and 34 inches high. How much wider is Paul's new couch?
   a. 4 inches wider
   b. 14 inches wider
   c. 40 inches wider

4. Nancy needs an air conditioner. Model A is $349. Model B is $369. Nancy has a $25 coupon for Model B. Which air conditioner is cheaper, and how much?
   a. Air Conditioner A is $5 cheaper.
   b. Air Conditioner A is $20 cheaper.
   c. Air Conditioner B is $5 cheaper.

Student's Name _____

Date _____

Balancing a Checkbook

Write the check information in the checkbook register and balance the checkbook.

Marie Louis		151
	DATE 4/28/09	
PAY TO THE ORDER OF Milton Electric Company		$ 53.50
Fifty-three and 50/100		Dollars
For 04-6627-88		Marie Louis
:2331572210 : 2 241536 7" 151		

Marie Louis		152
	DATE 4/28/09	
PAY TO THE ORDER OF Star Gas Company		$ 45.00
Forty-five and xx/100		Dollars
For 23452-001		Marie Louis
:2331572210 : 2 241536 7" 152		

Marie Louis		153
	DATE 5/1/09	
PAY TO THE ORDER OF Benson Realty		$ 750.00
Seven hundred fifity and xx/100		Dollars
For May's Rent		Marie Louis
:2331572210 : 2 241536 7" 153		

Marie Louis		154
	DATE 5/6/09	
PAY TO THE ORDER OF CCS Cable Company		$ 110.00
One hundred ten and xx/100		Dollars
For 64-452-02		Marie Louis
:2331572210 : 2 241536 7" 154		

Medical Associates Payroll Department	MID-CITY BANK		6258
PAY TO THE ORDER OF:	DATE		AMOUNT
Marie Louis 123 First Street Los Angeles, CA 12345	05/07/2009		$1,245.00
		C.W. Wilson AUTHORIZED SIGNATURE	
⑈746599331⑈88823422"6258"			

Marie Louis		155
	DATE 5/9/09	
PAY TO THE ORDER OF United Phone Services		$ 84.50
Eighty-four and 50/100		Dollars
For 205-775-3471		Marie Louis
:2331572210 : 2 241536 7" 155		

Number	Date	Transaction	Debit	Credit	Balance
150	4/21	Transworld Credit Card	850.50		753.50
	4/23	Paycheck		1,245.00	1,998.50
151	4/28	Milton Electric Company			
152	4/28		45.00		
153	5/1				
154	5/6				
	5/7	Paycheck		1,245.00	
155	5/9				

Student's Name _____

Date _____

Weights and Measurements: Using Postal Services

A. Look at the measurement chart and complete the sentences.

ITEM	SHAPE	LENGTH	HEIGHT
Letter		5 inch minimum 11-1/2 inch maximum	3-1/2 inch minimum 6-1/2 inch maximum
Large Envelope		11-1/2 inch minimum no maximum	6-1/2 inch minimum no maximum

1. Victor is mailing an item that is 13 inches long and 7 inches high. He's mailing _____.

   a. a letter   b. a large envelope

2. Max is mailing an item that is 11 1/2 inches long and 4 inches high. He's mailing _____.

   a. a letter   b. a large envelope

B. Look at the weight and rate chart. Write the correct cost.

First-Class Mail ™ Letters & Cards	
Weight	Rate
1 oz	$0.41
2 oz	$0.58
3 oz	$0.75
3.5 oz	$0.92

First-Class Mail ™ Large Envelopes			
Weight	Rate	Weight	Rate
1 oz	$0.80	5 oz	$1.48
2 oz	$0.97	6 oz	$1.65
3 oz	$1.14	7 oz	$1.82
4 oz	$1.31	8 oz	$1.99

First-Class Mail ™ Parcels			
Weight	Rate	Weight	Rate
1 oz	$1.13	5 oz	$1.81
2 oz	$1.30	6 oz	$1.98
3 oz	$1.47	7 oz	$2.15
4 oz	$1.64	8 oz	$2.32

1. How much does it cost to mail a 3 ounce letter?   _____

2. How much does it cost to mail a 3 ounce large envelope?   _____

3. How much does it cost to mail an 8 ounce parcel?   _____

4. How much does it cost to mail an 8 ounce large envelope?   _____

C. Look at the chart. Read the questions and choose the correct service.

SERVICE	Express Mail ™	First-Class Mail ™	Priority Mail ™
SHAPE & WEIGHT	 70 lbs or less	 3.5 oz or less 13 oz or less	 13 oz – 70 lbs
SPEED	1–2 days	1–3 days	2–3 days

	Express	First-Class	Priority
1. The package weighs 10 pounds. It must arrive in 1 day.	☐	☐	☐
2. The letter weighs 9 ounces. It can arrive in 2 to 3 days.	☐	☐	☐
3. The letter weighs 10 ounces. It must arrive in 1 day.	☐	☐	☐
4. The package weighs 14 ounces. It can arrive in 2–3 days.	☐	☐	☐

Paycheck and Pay Stub

Look at the paycheck and pay stub and answer the questions.

Kelsey Company	Jill Higgins	Employee No. 5362		Pay Period 10/21/09
Earnings	**Rate**	**Hours**	**This Period**	**Year to Date**
Regular	10.00	40	400.00	16,200.00
Overtime	15.00	5	75.00	1,230.00
Gross Pay			475.00	17,430.00
Taxes & Deductions			**This Period**	**Year to Date**
Federal Tax			45.00	1,845.00
State Tax			20.00	820.00
FICA/Medicare			35.00	1,435.00
Health Plan			40.00	1,600.00
Total			140.00	5,700.00
Net Pay			335.00	11,730.00

12398

Kelsey Company

10/21/09

PAY TO **JILL HIGGINS**

$335.00

Three hundred thirty-five and no/100 dollars

Manuel Espinola

:746355261 : 36455670⊓ 12398

1. How many total hours did Jill work in this pay period? _____

2. How much did the company deduct this period for federal and state taxes? _____

3. How much did Jill pay for federal and state taxes year-to-date? _____

4. How much did the company deduct for FICA (Social Security)/Medicare and Jill's health plan in this pay period? _____

5. How much did Jill pay for FICA (Social Security)/Medicare and her health plan year-to-date? _____

6. Next pay period Jill will work only 35 hours at her regular rate. How much will her gross pay be? _____

7. If Jill works 40 hours at her regular pay rate and 10 hours at her overtime rate, how much money will she make in a week? _____

8. Jill makes $10 an hour in regular pay. Jill earned $16,200 in regular pay year-to-date. How many hours did she work at her regular pay rate year-to-date? _____

9. Next year Jill will get a raise of $.50 an hour. How much will she make in regular pay each week when she works 40 hours a week? _____

Student's Name _____

Date _____

Reading Tables

A. Look at the table and answer the questions.

Most Common Causes of Home Fires			
Cooking	32%	Another house on fire	4%
Heating System	16%	House electrical or lighting system	3%
Someone starting the fire on purpose	5%	Clothing washer or dryer	2%
Burning candles	4%	Someone playing with fire	2%
Smoking cigarettes	4%	Burning trash in a container	2%

1. 3% of all home fires begin with burning candles.   True   False

2. Cooking is the most common cause of a home fire.   True   False

3. People start 6 out of 100 home fires on purpose.   True   False

4. 16 out of 100 fires start because of the heating system.   True   False

5. Clothing washers and dryers have the same chance of   True   False
starting a fire as burning trash.

B. Look at the table and answer the questions.

State	Number of Hurricanes in 103 Years	Storms Per Year	State	Number of Hurricanes in 103 Years	Storms Per Year
Alabama	11	0.11	Mississippi	9	0.09
Connecticut	8	0.08	North Carolina	29	0.28
Florida	60	0.57	New York	9	0.09
Georgia	5	0.05	Rhode Island	5	0.05
Louisiana	27	0.26	South Carolina	15	0.14
Massachusetts	6	0.06	Texas	37	0.36
Maine	5	0.05	Virginia	4	0.04

1. Which state had 27 storms in 103 years? _____

2. Which states had five hurricanes each in 103 years?

_____   _____   _____

3. Which state had the fewest storms per year? _____

4. Which state had the most storms per year? _____

Student's Name _____

Date _____

Reading a Floor Plan

A. Look at the floor plan and answer the questions.

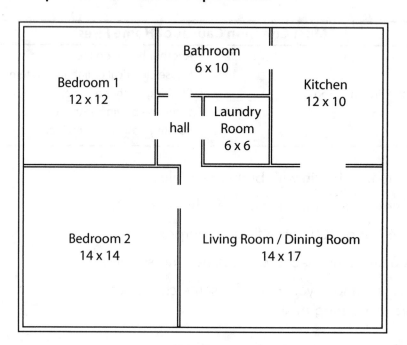

1. What is the biggest room in the apartment?
   a. Bedroom 1   b. the kitchen   c. the living room/dining room

2. What is the smallest room in the apartment?
   a. the laundry room   b. the bathroom   c. the kitchen

3. How do you find the square footage of Bedroom 1?
   a. 12 feet + 12 feet = 24 square feet
   b. 12 feet x 12 feet = 144 square feet
   c. 14 feet x 14 feet = 196 square feet

4. What is the square footage of the kitchen?
   a. 22 square feet   b. 60 square feet   c. 120 square feet

5. What is the square footage of the laundry room?
   a. 12 square feet   b. 24 square feet   c. 36 square feet

6. What is the square footage of the bathroom?
   a. 16 square feet   b. 60 square feet   c. 600 square feet

B. Measure a room in your home. What is the square footage?

_____ x _____ = _____

Student's Name _____

Date _____

Units of Measure

3 teaspoons = 1 tablespoon	1 cup = 1/2 pint
4 tablespoons = 1/4 cup	2 cups = 1 pint
8 tablespoons = 1/2 cup	2 pints = 1 quart
12 tablespoons = 3/4 cup	4 quarts = 1 gallon

A. Read the chart and answer the questions.

Alex is making a party fruit drink. He only has a teaspoon and a 1-pint measure.

1. The recipe requires 2 tablespoons of lemon juice. How many teaspoons is that?
   a. 2 teaspoons   b. 4 teaspoons   c. 6 teaspoons

2. The recipe requires 1/4 cup of sugar. How many teaspoons is that?
   a. 6 teaspoons   b. 12 teaspoons   c. 24 teaspoons

3. The recipe requires a cup of pineapple juice. How many pints is that?
   a. 1/2 pint   b. 1 pint   c. 1 1/2 pints

4. The recipe requires 2 quarts of orange juice. How many pints is that?
   a. 2 pints   b. 3 pints   c. 4 pints

B. Read the recipe and answer the questions.

 Pancake Recipe

For 12 pancakes
2 eggs
2 cups milk
1 teaspoon salt
3 cups flour
3 teaspoons baking powder
2 tablespoons oil

Mix the flour, baking powder, and salt together.
Mix the egg, milk, and oil together. Mix the wet and dry ingredients together.
For each pancake, pour a 1/4 cup of mixture in a hot pan.

1. What is the recipe for 6 pancakes?

_____ egg
_____ cup milk
_____ teaspoon salt
_____ cups flour
_____ teaspoons baking powder
_____ tablespoon oil

2. What is the recipe for 24 pancakes?

_____ eggs
_____ pints milk
_____ teaspoons salt
_____ cups flour
_____ tablespoons baking powder
_____ cup oil

Student's Name _____

Date _____

Temperatures (Fahrenheit & Celsius); Elapsed Time

A. Look at the thermometer and match the temperatures.

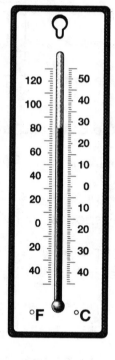

_____ **1.** 32° F   **a.** 15° C

_____ **2.** 90° F   **b.** 32° C

_____ **3.** 50° F   **c.** 0° C

_____ **4.** 14° F   **d.** 27° C

_____ **5.** 80° F   **e.** −10° C

_____ **6.** 0° F   **f.** 10° C

_____ **7.** 60° F   **g.** −16° C

B. Read the questions and circle the answers.

1. It's 8:15 AM. Josh will be driving until 1:00 PM. How much longer will he be driving?
a. 3 hours and 45 minutes
b. 4 hours and 15 minutes
c. 4 hours and 45 minutes

2. It's 11 PM. Pam will be working until 6:30 AM. How much longer will she be working?
a. 7 1/2 hours
b. 8 hours
c. 8 1/2 hours

3. It's 10:45. Debbie will be exercising until 11:25. How much longer will she be exercising?
a. 30 minutes
b. 40 minutes
c. 45 minutes

4. It's 11:45 AM. Kerry will be working for 3 1/2 more hours. When will she stop working?
a. 2:45 PM
b. 3:00 PM
c. 3:15 PM

5. It's 5:45 PM. Andy's cake needs to bake for 55 more minutes. When will he be taking the cake out of the oven?
a. 6:40 PM
b. 6:45 PM
c. 6:50 PM

6. It's 9:10 AM. The students will be taking a test for the next 3 hours and 45 minutes. What time will the test end?
a. 12:55 AM
b. 12:55 PM
c. 1:35 PM

Student's Name _____

Date _____

Word Problems about Rent Using Multiple Operations

Read the apartment ads and answer the questions.

Large 2 BEDROOM APARTMENT	1 BEDROOM APARTMENT NEAR PARK
Sunny kitchen and dining room. New appliances. $1,200/month. 12-month lease. 1 month security deposit required. Available NOW. 1438 Central Ave. 426-763-9900.	Large living room. Washer and dryer in basement. $900 monthly rent. Security deposit: 2 months rent. Two-year lease. Avail. 7/1/09.

1. How much will someone pay for a year of rent in the two-bedroom apartment?
   a. $12,000
   b. $14,400
   c. $24,000

2. Three friends are looking at the two-bedroom apartment. If they rent it, they will share the cost equally. How much will each person pay per month?
   a. $300
   b. $400
   c. $4,800

3. The Carters rented the apartment. They paid a plumber $175 to repair the kitchen sink, and they deducted this amount from last month's rent. How much rent did they pay last month?
   a. $925
   b. $975
   c. $1,025

4. The Carters will stay in this apartment next year, but they will have to pay an additional 10% for the rent. How much will the monthly rent be next year?
   a. $1,320
   b. $1,380
   c. $1,410

5. How much will someone pay for a year of rent in the one-bedroom apartment?
   a. $9,900
   b. $10,600
   c. $10,800

6. How much is the security deposit?
   a. $1,350
   b. $1,800
   c. $1,900

7. Ana rented the apartment from the first day it was available. When does her lease end?
   a. 6/30/10
   b. 6/30/11
   c. 6/30/12

8. Ana paid a locksmith $250 to fix the apartment door lock. She deducted this amount from last month's rent. How much rent did she pay last month?
   a. $650
   b. $700
   c. $750

Side by Side Plus 2
Number Practice Worksheets Answer Key

UNIT 1

1. Monday, June 7
2. Tuesday, June 8
3. Thursday, June 17
4. Wednesday, June 30
5. 06/10/1988
6. 06/14/1968
7. 06/23/1996
8. 06/18/1960
9. 06/20/1983
10. 06/05/1958

UNIT 2

1. 30 minutes
2. 6 hours
3. 3 hours
4. 3 hours and 45 minutes
5. 3 hours
6. 45 minutes
7. 2 hours and 15 minutes

UNIT 3

A.
1. $14.50
2. $5.50
3. $3.88
4. $10.25

B.
1. Ray's
2. Green's
3. Ray's
4. Green's
5. Green's
6. Ray's

UNIT 4

1. b
2. c
3. a
4. b
5. c
6. c
7. b
8. a

UNIT 5

A.
1. c
2. b
3. a
4. d
5. a
6. b

B.
1. b
2. a
3. b
4. c

UNIT 6

Number	Date	Transaction	Debit	Credit	Balance
150	4/21	Transworld Credit Card	850.50		753.50
	4/23	Paycheck		1,245.00	1,998.50
151	4/28	Milton Electric Company	53.50		1,945.00
152	4/28	Star Gas Company	45.00		1,900.00
153	5/1	Benson Realty	750.00		1,150.00
154	5/6	CCS Cable Company	110.00		1,040.00
	5/7	Paycheck		1,245.00	2,285.00
155	5/9	United Phone Service	84.50		2,200.50

UNIT 7

A.
1. b
2. a

B.
1. $0.75
2. $1.14
3. $2.32
4. $1.99

C.
1. Express
2. First Class
3. Express
4. Priority

UNIT 8

1. 45 hours
2. $65.00
3. $2,665.00
4. $75.00
5. $3,035.00
6. $350.00
7. $550.00
8. 1,620 hours
9. $420.00

UNIT 9

A.
1. False
2. True
3. False
4. True
5. True

B.
1. Louisiana
2. Georgia, Maine, Rhode Island
3. Virginia
4. Florida

UNIT 10

A.
1. c
2. a
3. b
4. c
5. c
6. b

B.
(Answers will vary.)

UNIT 11

A.
1. c
2. b
3. a
4. c

B.
1.
   - 1 egg
   - 1 cup milk
   - 1/2 teaspoon salt
   - 1 1/2 cups flour
   - 1 1/2 teaspoons baking powder
   - 1 tablespoon oil
2.
   - 4 eggs
   - 2 pints milk
   - 2 teaspoons salt
   - 6 cups flour
   - 2 tablespoons baking powder
   - 1/4 cup oil

UNIT 12

A.
1. c
2. b
3. f
4. e
5. d
6. g
7. a

B.
1. c
2. a
3. b
4. c
5. a
6. b

UNIT 13

1. b
2. b
3. c
4. a
5. c
6. b
7. b
8. a

FOOD SHOPPING

Read the article on text page 27 and answer the questions.

1. In the past, people shopped _____.
   A. at supermarkets
   B. online
   C. at open markets
   D. at wholesale stores

2. Today people don't have to shop every day because _____.
   A. they have refrigerators
   B. they have busy lives
   C. many stores sell food at low prices
   D. it's difficult to keep food fresh

3. *Enormous* in paragraph 3 means very _____.
   A. cheap
   B. large
   C. modern
   D. busy

4. People shop at wholesale stores because _____.
   A. the stores deliver food to their homes
   B. the food is always very fresh
   C. they don't like large stores
   D. they want to save money

5. Open markets are always _____.
   A. outside
   B. in the city
   C. open 24 hours a day
   D. small

6. Today most people shop for food _____.
   A. almost every day
   B. on the Internet
   C. once or twice a week
   D. every day

7. In paragraph 3, *people still shop in little food stores* means _____.
   A. they like to shop in little food stores
   B. they can't shop in little food stores
   C. they rarely shop in little food stores
   D. they shopped in little food stores in the past, and they shop in them now

8. The main idea of this article is that _____.
   A. refrigerators keep food fresh
   B. people shop for food in different ways
   C. today's stores sell food at low prices
   D. it's convenient to shop on the Internet

ANSWERS

1. Ⓐ Ⓑ Ⓒ Ⓓ
2. Ⓐ Ⓑ Ⓒ Ⓓ
3. Ⓐ Ⓑ Ⓒ Ⓓ
4. Ⓐ Ⓑ Ⓒ Ⓓ

5. Ⓐ Ⓑ Ⓒ Ⓓ
6. Ⓐ Ⓑ Ⓒ Ⓓ
7. Ⓐ Ⓑ Ⓒ Ⓓ
8. Ⓐ Ⓑ Ⓒ Ⓓ

A. WHICH WORD?

Choose the correct word.

1. I'd like a slice of (chili   pizza) with extra cheese.

2. Would you like some butter on your (bagel   donut)?

3. Would you like some ketchup on your (pizza   hamburger)?

4. I'd like a cheese (sandwich   taco) on whole wheat bread.

5. I'm having a (bowl of chili   muffin) for breakfast.

6. (Donuts   Hamburgers) have too much sugar.

7. Would you like a beef or a chicken (muffin   taco)?

8. I can't eat that (bagel   hot dog). I don't eat meat.

B. CROSSWORD

Across

2.

3.

4.

7.

8.

Down

1.   5.

6.

Student's Name _____

Date _____

ONE DAY'S FOOD
Look at the Fact File on text page 27 and answer the questions.

1. Hens produce _____.
   A. rice
   B. cocoa
   C. eggs
   D. chocolate

2. According to the fact file, the world produces more than _____ a day.
   A. 200,000,000,000 eggs
   B. 2,000,000,000 eggs
   C. 200,000,000 eggs
   D. 20,000,000 eggs

3. It takes 8,818 tons of cocoa beans to make _____ chocolate bars.
   A. 7,000,000
   B. 70,000,000
   C. 700,000,000
   D. 7,000,000,000

4. The world produces _____ tons of rice a day.
   A. 1,000,006
   B. 1,000,600
   C. 1,000,060
   D. 1,600,000

5. Cyprus is a very large _____.
   A. city
   B. pyramid
   C. island
   D. omelet

6. The world produces more than a million and a half _____ every day.
   A. tons of cocoa beans
   B. tons of rice
   C. tons of chocolate bars
   D. tons of cocoa bars

7. The world produces _____ pounds of cocoa beans every day. (There are 2,000 pounds in a ton.)
   A. 8,818
   B. 17,636
   C. 700,000,000
   D. 17,636,000

8. According to the fact file, the world produces more than _____ in a week.
   A. 14 billion eggs
   B. 70,000 tons of cocoa
   C. 14 million tons of rice
   D. 7 billion chocolate bars

ANSWERS

1. (A) (B) (C) (D)   5. (A) (B) (C) (D)
2. (A) (B) (C) (D)   6. (A) (B) (C) (D)
3. (A) (B) (C) (D)   7. (A) (B) (C) (D)
4. (A) (B) (C) (D)   8. (A) (B) (C) (D)

Student's Name _____

Date _____

A. DID YOU KNOW?

Read the article on text page 59 and answer the questions.

1. The _____ is in New York City.
   A. biggest igloo in the world
   B. longest car in the world
   C. biggest costume party in the world
   D. biggest subway station in the world

2. *Igloos* are _____.
   A. hotels that stay open in winter
   B. buildings made of hard snow
   C. hotels with many rooms
   D. Swedish hotels

3. More than 500,000 people _____.
   A. walk through Grand Central Terminal every day
   B. walk through the streets of Brazil in costumes every day during Carnival
   C. stay at the Ice Hotel every year
   D. ride in the world's longest car every day

4. In Brazil people wear _____ to celebrate Carnival.
   A. costume parties
   B. bathing suits
   C. costumes
   D. evening gowns

5. The longest car in the world _____.
   A. has a waterbed to swim in
   B. is twenty-six feet long
   C. is one hundred meters long
   D. has 13 wheels on each side

6. According to this article, the Ice Hotel _____.
   A. has a swimming pool
   B. starts to turn to water when it's warm
   C. always has 150 guests
   D. is popular in the spring

ANSWERS

1. (A) (B) (C) (D)   4. (A) (B) (C) (D)
2. (A) (B) (C) (D)   5. (A) (B) (C) (D)
3. (A) (B) (C) (D)   6. (A) (B) (C) (D)

B. THE LONGEST WORDS

Look in an English dictionary and in a dictionary in your language.

1. What's the longest word you can find in English? _____

2. What does it mean? _____

3. What's the longest word you can find in your language? _____

4. What does it mean? _____

5. How many letters are in each of these two words? _____

WORLD GEOGRAPHY FACTS

Look at the Fact File on text page 59 and answer the questions.

1. The largest ocean in the world is sixty-four million _____.
   A. miles long
   B. kilometers long
   C. square miles
   D. square kilometers

2. The longest river in the world is 4,180 _____ long.
   A. feet
   B. miles
   C. meters
   D. kilometers

3. Mount Everest is _____ meters high.
   A. four thousand one hundred eighty
   B. twenty-nine thousand twenty-eight
   C. six thousand six hundred ninety
   D. eight thousand eight hundred forty-eight

4. There are 1000 meters in a kilometer. Mount Everest is almost _____ high.
   A. nine kilometers
   B. eighty-nine kilometers
   C. eight hundred ninety kilometers
   D. eighty-eight kilometers

5. The Nile is six thousand six hundred ninety _____.
   A. miles long
   B. kilometers long
   C. miles high
   D. square kilometers

6. Sixty-four million square miles _____ 165,760,000 square kilometers.
   A. is a little more than
   B. is much more than
   C. isn't as much as
   D. is the same as

7. The Sahara _____ nine million square kilometers.
   A. is
   B. is less than
   C. is more than
   D. is much less than

8. The Pacific Ocean _____.
   A. is 165,760,000 kilometers long
   B. is larger than the Atlantic Ocean
   C. isn't as large as the Sahara desert
   D. isn't as large as the Atlantic Ocean

ANSWERS

1.	(A)	(B)	(C)	(D)	5.	(A)	(B)	(C)	(D)
2.	(A)	(B)	(C)	(D)	6.	(A)	(B)	(C)	(D)
3.	(A)	(B)	(C)	(D)	7.	(A)	(B)	(C)	(D)
4.	(A)	(B)	(C)	(D)	8.	(A)	(B)	(C)	(D)

A. WHICH PREFIX?

Complete the words with a negative prefix.

1. ___polite
2. ___safe
3. ___healthy
4. ___expensive
5. ___friendly
6. ___honest
7. ___comfortable
8. ___patient

B. WHICH WORD?

Choose the correct word from the answers in Exercise A.

1. I really don't need another shirt, but I'll buy this one because it's _____.
2. That car doesn't have any seat belts. Don't ride in it! It's _____!
3. Alex takes things in a store and doesn't pay for them. He's very _____.
4. There's too much sugar in those donuts. They're very _____.
5. I don't sleep well at night because my bed is _____.
6. Luis wants to learn to speak English right away. He's _____.
7. Don't talk when you have food in your mouth! It's _____.
8. People think Gloria is _____ because she's shy and likes to be alone.

C. PREFIX OR NO PREFIX?

Choose the correct word from Exercise A—either with or without a negative prefix.

1. Butter and sugar aren't good for you, but vegetables are _____.
2. Harvey always says thank you, but his brother Howard is very _____.
3. These shoes feel good on my feet, but those shoes are _____.
4. You can never believe anything Clara says, but her sister is very _____.
5. This dress doesn't cost a lot of money, but that dress is very _____.
6. Daniel can wait for hours and never get upset, but his son Steven is very

   _____.

7. George never smiles or says hello, but his brother Robert is very _____.
8. You won't have an accident in this car, but that car is _____.

YOU'RE HIRED

Read the article on text page 81 and answer the questions.

1. The interview advice in this article is from _____.
   A. job applicants
   B. personnel officers
   C. supervisors
   D. presidents of companies

2. According to this article, you should talk about _____ at a job interview.
   A. the salary
   B. your family
   C. your skills
   D. the interviewer

3. According to this article, you should _____ when you're at a job interview.
   A. write a thank-you note
   B. shake your head firmly
   C. speak loudly
   D. smile

4. At an interview you shouldn't be _____.
   A. enthusiastic
   B. confident
   C. shy
   D. neat

5. Make "eye contact" means _____.
   A. look at the interviewer
   B. look at the floor
   C. take off your glasses
   D. look around the room

6. Speak confidently means talk _____.
   A. softly
   B. quickly
   C. honestly
   D. about how well you can do the job

7. If you don't have experience, tell the interviewer that _____.
   A. you have experience
   B. you can learn quickly
   C. you're sorry
   D. the job is easy and you don't need experience

8. The ten tips for a job interview are _____.
   A. the same everywhere in the world
   B. ten things applicants should never do
   C. ten things applicants should do
   D. ten things applicants always do

ANSWERS

1. Ⓐ Ⓑ Ⓒ Ⓓ
2. Ⓐ Ⓑ Ⓒ Ⓓ
3. Ⓐ Ⓑ Ⓒ Ⓓ
4. Ⓐ Ⓑ Ⓒ Ⓓ
5. Ⓐ Ⓑ Ⓒ Ⓓ
6. Ⓐ Ⓑ Ⓒ Ⓓ
7. Ⓐ Ⓑ Ⓒ Ⓓ
8. Ⓐ Ⓑ Ⓒ Ⓓ

A. WHICH JOB?

Choose the job that is right for each person.

designer	director	gardener	photographer	programmer	supervisor

1. Tanya likes to plant flowers. _____

2. Eric is good with computers. He studied computer science. _____

3. Suzanne loves to take pictures. _____

4. Sonya worked as an assembler. She wants a better factory job. _____

5. Jean wants to make movies. _____

6. Richard loves to draw and paint. _____

B. CROSSWORD

Across

1.

3.

4.

6.

7.

Down

2.

4.

5.

FAMILIES AND TIME

Read the article on text page 103 and answer the questions.

1. According to the article, people today are spending less time _____.
   A. at work
   B. alone
   C. with their friends
   D. on the Internet

2. In the past in many countries, the mother didn't _____.
   A. shop
   B. take care of the children
   C. stay home
   D. go to work

3. This article talks about technology _____.
   A. for transportation
   B. for housework
   C. for communication
   D. for medicine

4. In paragraph 3, *many children come home from school to an empty apartment* means _____.
   A. there isn't any furniture in the apartment
   B. there aren't any adults at home
   C. the refrigerator is empty
   D. there aren't any toys for the children to play with

5. According to the article, in a single-parent family _____.
   A. the parent is very busy
   B. the parent stays home
   C. there is only one child
   D. both parents work

6. According to this article, technology _____.
   A. brings families closer together
   B. can make it difficult for families to communicate with each other
   C. is always bad
   D. is a problem for people who are far away

7. The main idea of paragraph 2 is _____.
   A. fathers work
   B. single parents have to do everything
   C. there are many single parents
   D. parents today don't have as much time for their children as in the past

8. An activity that this article does *NOT* talk about is _____.
   A. watching TV
   B. using the Internet
   C. listening to CDs
   D. talking on the phone

ANSWERS

1.	Ⓐ Ⓑ Ⓒ Ⓓ		**5.**	Ⓐ Ⓑ Ⓒ Ⓓ	
2.	Ⓐ Ⓑ Ⓒ Ⓓ		**6.**	Ⓐ Ⓑ Ⓒ Ⓓ	
3.	Ⓐ Ⓑ Ⓒ Ⓓ		**7.**	Ⓐ Ⓑ Ⓒ Ⓓ	
4.	Ⓐ Ⓑ Ⓒ Ⓓ		**8.**	Ⓐ Ⓑ Ⓒ Ⓓ	

COUNTRIES WHERE PEOPLE SPEND THE MOST TIME AT WORK
Look at the Fact File on text page 103 and answer the questions.

1. The average person in France works _____ hours per year.
   A. one thousand five hundred sixty
   B. one thousand six hundred fifty-six
   C. one thousand nine hundred sixty-six
   D. one thousand eight-hundred ninety-nine

2. The average person in the United States doesn't work as many hours as the average person in _____.
   A. France
   B. Japan
   C. Germany
   D. Thailand

3. The average person in _____ works 310 more hours per year than the average person in France.
   A. Thailand
   B. the United States
   C. Japan
   D. Germany

4. The average person in Thailand works 311 more hours per year than the average person in _____.
   A. the United States
   B. France
   C. Japan
   D. Germany

5. The average person in France works _____ per year than the average person in Germany.
   A. 96 more hours
   B. 4 more hours
   C. 104 more hours
   D. 116 more hours

6. The country where people spend the most time at work is in _____.
   A. North America
   B. South America
   C. Europe
   D. Asia

7. If the average person in Thailand works fifty weeks per year, he or she works _____.
   A. forty hours per week
   B. forty-two hours per week
   C. forty-four hours per week
   D. forty-five hours per week

8. If the average person in the United States works 50 weeks a year, he or she works almost _____.
   A. 45 hours a week
   B. 40 hours a week
   C. 35 hours a week
   D. 30 hours a week

ANSWERS

1. Ⓐ Ⓑ Ⓒ Ⓓ   5. Ⓐ Ⓑ Ⓒ Ⓓ
2. Ⓐ Ⓑ Ⓒ Ⓓ   6. Ⓐ Ⓑ Ⓒ Ⓓ
3. Ⓐ Ⓑ Ⓒ Ⓓ   7. Ⓐ Ⓑ Ⓒ Ⓓ
4. Ⓐ Ⓑ Ⓒ Ⓓ   8. Ⓐ Ⓑ Ⓒ Ⓓ

GAZETTE 4
Worksheet 3: Build Your Vocabulary

Student's Name _____

Date _____

A. CATEGORIZATION

Write these words in the correct categories.

coffee maker	garbage disposal	microwave
dishwasher	iron	toaster
dryer		washing machine

Appliances for Clothing Care

_____

_____

_____

Appliances for Food Preparation

_____

_____

_____

Appliances for Food Cleanup

_____

_____

_____

B. WHICH WORD?

Choose the correct word.

coffee maker	dryer	iron	toaster	washer
dishwasher	garbage disposal	microwave	vacuum cleaner	

1. After you wash the clothes, put them in the _____.

2. You can throw that old food in the sink. We have a _____.

3. It'll take only five minutes to cook those vegetables in the _____.

4. The _____ is broken. I have to wash those glasses in the sink.

5. Can I put this blouse in the _____, or should I wash it by hand?

6. This floor is very dirty. Where's the _____?

7. I can't wear this shirt. It looks terrible. I need the _____.

8. We don't have a _____. We'll have to eat our jam on cold bread.

9. Put four cups of water in the _____.

Student's Name _____

Date _____

COMMUNITIES

Read the article on text page 137 and answer the questions.

1. In suburban communities, people usually live _____.
   A. far from a city
   B. in apartment buildings
   C. in separate houses
   D. on busy streets

2. In rural communities, people often live _____.
   A. near public transportation
   B. in apartment buildings
   C. in neighborhoods
   D. far from their neighbors

3. In urban communities, people DON'T live _____.
   A. close together
   B. in neighborhoods
   C. in the countryside
   D. in small houses

4. If you live in a rural area, the usual way to get to places is to _____.
   A. walk
   B. drive
   C. take the bus
   D. take the train

5. In the past, most people lived in _____.
   A. urban communities
   B. megacities
   C. suburban communities
   D. rural areas

6. According to the experts, in the future people will live in _____.
   A. very large suburban communities
   B. very large urban communities
   C. very large rural communities
   D. cities with one or two million people

7. In paragraph 5, *people keep to themselves* means _____.
   A. they aren't friendly with their neighbors
   B. they're dishonest
   C. they spend very little money
   D. they work hard

8. In the last paragraph, *time will tell* means _____.
   A. future communities will be friendly
   B. future communities won't be friendly
   C. we'll have to wait and see if future communities are friendly
   D. we'll have to wait and see if the experts are right

ANSWERS

1. (A) (B) (C) (D)
2. (A) (B) (C) (D)
3. (A) (B) (C) (D)
4. (A) (B) (C) (D)

5. (A) (B) (C) (D)
6. (A) (B) (C) (D)
7. (A) (B) (C) (D)
8. (A) (B) (C) (D)

THE TEN LARGEST CITIES IN THE WORLD: 1950 AND 2010

Look at the Fact File on text page 137 and answer the questions.

1. In 2010 the largest city in the world will have about _____ people.
   A. 20 million
   B. 25 million
   C. 27 million
   D. 29 million

2. In 2010 _____ will have about 25 million people.
   A. Shanghai
   B. São Paulo
   C. Tokyo
   D. Lagos

3. _____ wasn't one of the world's 10 largest cities in 1950, but it will be in 2010.
   A. Calcutta
   B. Tokyo
   C. Beijing
   D. Buenos Aires

4. In 1950 Shanghai and _____ had about the same number of people.
   A. Tokyo
   B. Moscow
   C. Lagos
   D. Calcutta

5. In 1950 the largest city in the world had about _____ people.
   A. 8 million
   B. 9 million
   C. 12 million
   D. 15 million

6. In 2010 New York will have a larger population than _____.
   A. London
   B. Lagos
   C. Mumbai
   D. Mexico City

7. In 2010 _____ countries will have more than 20 million people.
   A. four
   B. five
   C. six
   D. seven

8. In 2010 Tokyo will have about _____ more people than it did in 1950.
   A. 12 million
   B. 17 million
   C. 22 million
   D. 25 million

ANSWERS

1. A B C D
2. A B C D
3. A B C D
4. A B C D

5. A B C D
6. A B C D
7. A B C D
8. A B C D

A. CROSSWORD

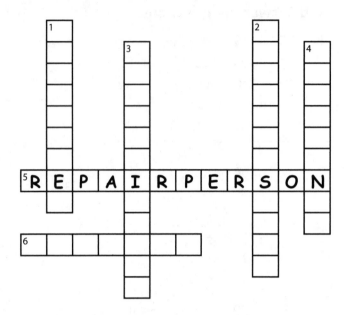

Across

5. If your TV isn't working, call a TV _____.

6. If the outside of your house looks old and dirty, call a house _____.

Down

1. If you want cable TV, call a cable TV _____.

2. If your chimney is dirty, call a _____.

3. If there are cockroaches in your apartment, call an _____.

4. If your refrigerator is broken, call an _____ repairperson.

B. WHO WILL THEY CALL?

1. Alexander is afraid to light a fire in his fireplace. He's going to call

(an appliance repairperson   a chimneysweep).

2. Carol's TV is broken. She's calling a (TV repairperson   cable TV installer).

3. Ed has mice in his basement. He's calling (an exterminator   a chimneysweep).

4. The Smith family wants to get more TV channels. The cable TV company will send

(a TV repairperson   an installer) to their apartment.

5. Jennifer's dishwasher is making terrible noises. She's going to call an

(exterminator   appliance repairperson).

Side by Side Plus 2
Gazette Worksheets Answer Key

GAZETTE 1
Worksheet 1: Reading

1. C
2. A
3. B
4. D
5. A
6. C
7. D
8. B

Worksheet 2: Build Your Vocabulary

A.
1. pizza
2. bagel
3. hamburger
4. sandwich
5. muffin
6. Donuts
7. taco
8. hot dog

B.

Worksheet 3: Fact File

1. C
2. B
3. C
4. D
5. C
6. B
7. D
8. A

GAZETTE 2
Worksheet 1: Reading

A.
1. D
2. B
3. A
4. C
5. D
6. B

B.
(Answers will vary.)

Worksheet 2: Fact File

1. C
2. B
3. D
4. A
5. B
6. D
7. C
8. B

Worksheet 3: Build Your Vocabulary

A.
1. im
2. un
3. un
4. in
5. un
6. dis
7. un
8. im

B.
1. inexpensive
2. unsafe
3. dishonest
4. unhealthy
5. uncomfortable
6. impatient
7. impolite
8. unfriendly

C.
1. healthy
2. impolite
3. uncomfortable
4. honest
5. expensive
6. impatient

7. friendly
8. unsafe

GAZETTE 3
Worksheet 1: Reading

1. B
2. C
3. D
4. C
5. A
6. D
7. B
8. C

Worksheet 2: Build Your Vocabulary

A.
1. gardener
2. programmer
3. photographer
4. supervisor
5. director
6. designer

B.

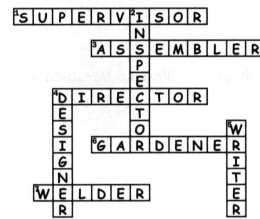

GAZETTE 4
Worksheet 1: Reading

1. C
2. D
3. C
4. B
5. A
6. B
7. D
8. C

Worksheet 2: Fact File

1. B
2. D

3. B
4. C
5. A
6. D
7. C
8. B

Worksheet 3: Build Your Vocabulary

A.
Appliances for Clothing Care:
  dryer
  iron
  washing machine

Appliances for Food Preparation:
  coffee maker
  microwave
  toaster

Appliances for Food Cleanup:
  dishwasher
  garbage disposal

B.
1. dryer
2. garbage disposal
3. microwave
4. dishwasher
5. washer
6. vacuum cleaner
7. iron
8. toaster
9. coffee maker

GAZETTE 5
Worksheet 1: Reading

1. C
2. D
3. C
4. B
5. D
6. B
7. A
8. C

Worksheet 2: Fact File

1. D
2. B
3. C
4. B
5. C
6. A
7. B
8. C

Worksheet 3: Build Your Vocabulary

A.

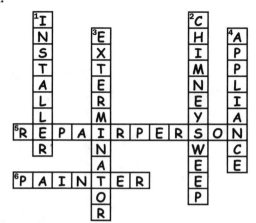

B.

1. a chimneysweep
2. TV repairperson
3. an exterminator
4. an installer
5. appliance repairperson

Side by Side Plus 2
Life Skills Worksheets

The *Side by Side Plus 2* Life Skills Worksheets provide realia-based reading and writing activities including forms, diagrams, charts, schedules, classified ads, store directories, food labels, clothing labels, receipts, invitations, advertisements, product warning labels, medicine labels, checks, telephone directories, a calendar, a pay stub, an accident report, and a rental agreement. The worksheets are fully coordinated with the *Side by Side Plus* units to offer valuable supplemental practice in class or at home for all students or for those students who require additional support or enrichment.

Unit 1
1 Dates and Forms
2 Reading a Community Calendar
3 The American Education System

Unit 2
4 School Personnel & Locations
5 Reading a School Floor Plan
6 Parts of a Computer

Unit 3
7 Locating Items in a Supermarket
8 Counting U.S. Currency; Reading a Receipt
9 Reading a Food Label
10 Units of Measure for Food

Unit 4
11 Offers and Invitations
12 Reading Invitations

Unit 5
13 Comparing Computers
14 Reading an Ad

Unit 6
15 Clothing Labels
16 Returning a Store Item
17 Using an ATM
18 Reading and Writing a Check

Unit 7
19 Business Schedules
20 Reading a Train Schedule

Unit 8
21 Work Skills and a Job Application
22 Requesting a Schedule Change
23 Help Wanted Ads
24 Reading a Pay Stub
25 Reading an Accident Report

Unit 9
26 Emergencies at Home
27 First Aid
28 Reading a Warning Label
29 Safety Procedures

Unit 10
30 Renting an Apartment
31 Reading Apartment Ads
32 Rules and Regulations Checklist

Unit 11
33 Parts of the Face and Body
34 Reading Medicine Labels
35 Nutrition; Medical History Form

Unit 12
36 A Telephone Bill
37 Telephone Directory
38 Reading the Yellow Pages

Unit 13
39 Requesting Apartment Maintenance or Repairs
40 Reading a Rental Agreement
41 Rights and Responsibilities

Student's Name _____

Date _____

Dates and Forms

A. Look at the abbreviations. Write the days and months.

1. WED _____

2. MON _____

3. SAT _____

4. TUES _____

5. FRI _____

6. THURS _____

7. SUN _____

8. MAR _____

9. OCT _____

10. JAN _____

11. MAY _____

12. NOV _____

13. FEB _____

14. JUL _____

15. AUG _____

16. DEC _____

17. JUN _____

18. APR _____

19. SEP _____

B. Write the dates in numbers.

1. January 8, 2009   _ _ / _ _ / _ _

2. July 10, 2010   _ _ / _ _ / _ _

3. March 12, 2008   _ _ / _ _ / _ _

4. May 3, 2006   _ _ / _ _ / _ _

5. September 5, 2007   _ _ / _ _ / _ _

6. November 30, 2012   _ _ / _ _ / _ _

7. April 9, 2011   _ _ / _ _ / _ _

8. February 22, 2009   _ _ / _ _ / _ _

9. August 1, 1981   _ _ / _ _ / _ _

10. October 2, 2008   _ _ / _ _ / _ _

11. December 6, 2010   _ _ / _ _ / _ _

12. June 4, 1997   _ _ / _ _ / _ _

C. Complete the registration form with your own information.

NAME	Last	First

ADDRESS — Number Street — Apartment

City — State — Zip Code

DATE OF BIRTH — mm dd yyyy — AGE

Reading a Community Calendar

North Central Community Center – Calendar of Events						
October						
Sunday	**Monday**	**Tuesday**	**Wednesday**	**Thursday**	**Friday**	**Saturday**
		1 Kids Exercise Class	2	3 Cooking Class	4	5 Swimming Lessons
6	7	8 Kids Exercise Class	9	10	11 Movie Night	12
13	14 Internet Class	15 Kids Exercise Class	16	17 Cooking Class	18	19 Swimming Lessons
20	(21)	22 Kids Exercise Class	23	24	25 Movie Night	26 Hiking Club
27	28 Internet Class	29 Kids Exercise Class	30	31		

A. Look at the calendar. Circle T for True or F for False.

1. Movie Night is on the second and fourth Friday of the month.   T   F
2. There's an Internet class on the first and third Monday of the month.   T   F
3. Swimming lessons are on the second and fourth Saturday of the month. T   F
4. The exercise class for children is every Thursday.   T   F
5. The Hiking Club meets on the fourth Saturday of the month.   T   F
6. There are cooking classes the first and third Tuesday of the month.   T   F

B. There are also other events in October. Look at the calendar and circle the dates.

1. There's a Book Club meeting on the third Monday of the month.
2. There's a music concert on the fourth Sunday of the month.
3. There's a Halloween party on 10/31.
4. There's a Columbus Day breakfast on 10/12.
5. There's an exercise class for seniors 65 years and over every Wednesday.
6. There's a dance party on the third Friday of the month.

Student's Name _____

Date _____

The American Education System

A. Match the schools with their definitions.

____ **1.** pre-school

a. a school for children in kindergarten to 5th grades

____ **2.** middle school

b. a school for young children before kindergarten

____ **3.** elementary school

c. a school for teenagers in 9th to 12th grades

____ **4.** high school

d. a school for children in 6th to 8th grades

____ **5.** university

e. a two-year school for students who finished high school

____ **6.** college

f. a school for students who finished a four-year college

____ **7.** community college

g. a school with a college and a graduate school

____ **8.** graduate school

h. a four-year school for students who finished high school

B. Number the schools in their order from lowest (1) to highest (6).

____ graduate school

____ middle school

____ pre-school

____ elementary school

____ high school

____ college

Student's Name _____
Date _____

School Personnel & Locations

A. Complete the sentences with the correct words.

auditorium	gym	nurse's office
cafeteria	hall	principal's office
guidance office	library	school office

1. The school nurse works in the _____.

2. The P.E. teacher works in the _____.

3. The librarian works in the _____.

4. The cafeteria workers work in the _____.

5. The security officer works in the _____.

6. The school secretary works in the _____.

7. The guidance counselor works in the _____.

8. The principal works in the _____.

9. The music teacher works in the _____.

B. Match the school personnel with the work they do.

____ 1. The school nurse   a. makes sure the school is safe.

____ 2. The P.E. teacher   b. helps students choose their classes.

____ 3. The librarian   c. manages the school office.

____ 4. The cafeteria workers   d. serve food to the students.

____ 5. The security officer   e. teaches physical education.

____ 6. The principal   f. manages the library.

____ 7. The school secretary   g. manages the whole school.

____ 8. The guidance counselor   h. takes care of students when they feel sick.

Student's Name _____

Date _____

Reading a School Floor Plan

Look at the Milford Middle School Floor Plan. Circle T for True or F for False.

Milford Middle School

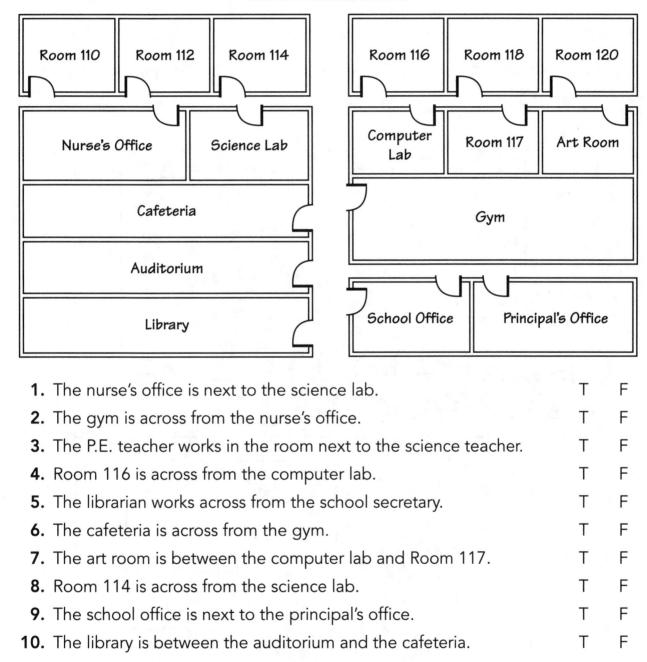

1.	The nurse's office is next to the science lab.	T F
2.	The gym is across from the nurse's office.	T F
3.	The P.E. teacher works in the room next to the science teacher.	T F
4.	Room 116 is across from the computer lab.	T F
5.	The librarian works across from the school secretary.	T F
6.	The cafeteria is across from the gym.	T F
7.	The art room is between the computer lab and Room 117.	T F
8.	Room 114 is across from the science lab.	T F
9.	The school office is next to the principal's office.	T F
10.	The library is between the auditorium and the cafeteria.	T F

Student's Name _____

Date _____

Parts of a Computer

Look at the diagram. Find the items in the list below. Write the correct letter next to each item.

_____ **1.** CPU

_____ **2.** Ethernet cable

_____ **3.** Ethernet port

_____ **4.** keyboard

_____ **5.** monitor

_____ **6.** monitor cable

_____ **7.** mouse

_____ **8.** mouse cable

_____ **9.** power button

_____ **10.** power cable

_____ **11.** power cable port

_____ **12.** USB port

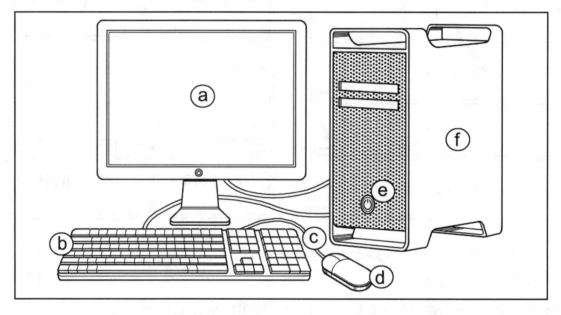

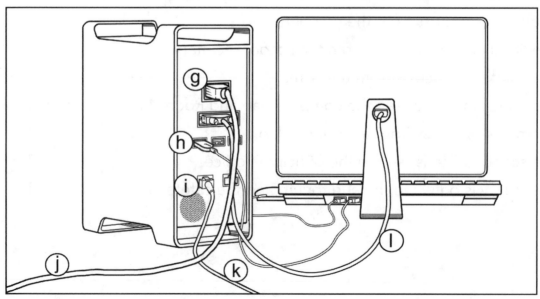

Locating Items in a Supermarket

Look at the supermarket directory. Complete the conversation.

Supermarket Directory	
Dairy	Aisle 1
Baked Goods	Aisle 2
Beverages	Aisle 3
Frozen Foods	Aisle 4
Meat	Aisle 5
Produce	Aisle 6

1. A. Excuse me. Where are the strawberries?

   B. They're in the _____ section, Aisle _____.

2. A. Excuse me. Where's the yogurt?

   B. It's in the _____ section, Aisle _____.

3. A. Excuse me. Where's the soda?

   B. It's in the _____ section, Aisle _____.

4. A. Excuse me. Where's the bread?

   B. It's in the _____ section, Aisle _____.

5. A. Excuse me. Where's the ice cream?

   B. It's in the _____ section, Aisle _____.

6. A. Excuse me. Where are the apple pies?

   B. They're in the _____ section, Aisle _____.

7. A. Excuse me. Where's the chicken?

   B. It's in the _____ section, Aisle _____.

8. A. Excuse me. Where are the mushrooms?

   B. They're in the _____ section, Aisle _____.

Counting U.S. Currency; Reading a Receipt

A. Write the amount.

1. _____ _____

2. _____ _____

3. _____

4. _____

5. _____

6. _____

B. Look at the supermarket receipt. Answer the questions.

```
        ( Food Land )

1 LB. @ $2.99 LB.
MUSHROOMS                  2.99
ICE CREAM 1 QT.            3.49
3 LBS. @ $1.50 LB
APPLES                     4.50
4 @ $.25
BANANAS                    1.00
3 LBS. @ $1.99 LB
CHICKEN                    5.97
MILK 1 GAL.                3.99
3 @ $1.00
SOUP                       3.00
....................................
             TOTAL       $24.94
             CASH        $25.00
             CHANGE        $.06
```

1. The person spent _____ on mushrooms.

2. A pound of chicken costs _____.

3. Three pounds of apples cost _____.

4. One banana costs _____.

5. Three cans of soup cost _____.

6. This person bought a _____ of milk and a _____ of ice cream.

7. This person spent _____ at the store

Reading a Food Label

Read the food label. Answer the questions.

Fruit Yogurt
Nutrition Facts
Serving Size 1 cup
Servings per Container 2

Calories 240	Calories from Fat 25
	% Daily Value
Total Fat 3 g	4%
Cholesterol 15 mg	5%
Sodium 140 mg	6%
Total Carbohydrate 46 g	15%

| Vitamin A | 10% | • | Vitamin C | 4% |
| Calcium | 35% | • | Iron | 0% |

Keep Refrigerated

1. How much is one serving?

   a. one cup   b. two cups   c. a container

2. How many servings are in the container?

   a. one cup   b. two cups   c. one quart

3. How many vitamins are in this yogurt?

   a. one   b. two   c. three

4. How much fat is in one serving of this yogurt?

   a. 25   b. three milligrams   c. three grams

5. How many calories are in each serving?

   a. 120   b. 240   c. 480

6. Where do you keep this yogurt?

   a. in the refrigerator   b. in the freezer   c. on the counter

Student's Name _____

Date _____

Units of Measure for Food

Liquid Measures		Weights
3 teaspoons = 1 tablespoon	1 pint = 2 cups = 16 fluid ounces	4 ounces = 1/4 pound
2 tablespoons = 1 fluid ounce	1 quart = 2 pints = 32 fluid ounces	8 ounces = 1/2 pound
4 tablespoons = 1/4 cup	4 quarts = 1 gallon = 128 fluid ounces	16 ounces = one pound
1 cup = 8 fluid ounces		

A. Look at the chart above. Write the words for these abbreviations.

1. fl. oz. _____fluid ounce_____

2. tsp. _____

3. c. _____

4. Tbsp. _____

5. gal. _____

6. qt. _____

7. pt. _____

8. lb. _____

B. Put the following units of measure in order from smallest (1) to largest (7).

_____ one cup

_____ one tablespoon

_____ one fluid ounce

_____ one gallon

_____ one pint

___1__ one teaspoon

_____ one quart

C. Look at the recipe on the left. Then complete the recipe on the right.

Party Punch (makes 15 servings)	Party Punch (makes 30 servings)
2 quarts orange juice	1 __gallon__ orange juice
1 qt. lemon/lime soda	1/2 _____ lemon/lime soda
1 c. lemon juice	1 _____ lemon juice
1 pt. pineapple juice	1 _____ pineapple juice
8 ozs. frozen strawberries	1 _____ frozen strawberries

Offers and Invitations

Choose the most appropriate response.

1. Would you like some more ice cream?
   a. No, thank you.
   b. I'm sorry. I can't.
   c. Yes. I'd love to.

2. Would you like some cookies?
   a. I can't. I'm sorry.
   b. Yes. I'd love to.
   c. Yes. Thanks.

3. Would you like to have lunch with my family this weekend?
   a. Yes. I have to work this weekend.
   b. Yes. I'd love to.
   c. Thank you. I'm sorry.

4. Would you like to go out for coffee this afternoon?
   a. Yes. I'm sorry. I can't.
   b. No.
   c. I'm sorry. I can't. I have to get home.

5. Would you like some more dessert?
   a. Yes. Thanks.
   b. Yes. I'd love to.
   c. Yes. I have to eat fruit.

6. Would you like to go out for dinner tonight?
   a. Thanks. I can't.
   b. I'm sorry. I can't. I have to work.
   c. Thank you. I'm sorry.

Reading Invitations

Read the invitation. Circle T for True or F for False.

Please join us as our daughter

Lisa Johnson

graduates from Jameson College

Saturday, June 1
at 4:00 in the afternoon
Jameson Hall

Party following the ceremony
at our home:
121 Longwood Road
Longwood Lake, Michigan

RSVP by May 19
kjohnson@worldmail.net

1. Lisa Johnson is graduating from high school.   T   F

2. The party invitation is from Lisa Johnson.   T   F

3. The ceremony and the party are at the same place.   T   F

4. The party is after the ceremony.   T   F

5. The party is at the Johnsons' house.   T   F

6. The ceremony is in the evening.   T   F

7. You need to answer the invitation by June 1.   T   F

8. You need to answer the invitation by e-mail.   T   F

Comparing Computers

Read the computer ads. Use the following adjectives (or any others you wish) to complete the recommendations below.

cheap	fast	light	reliable
easy-to-use	large	powerful	small

PB1000 Laptop

Stay with the Open Doors system — used for many years.

Great for schoolwork, office work, and e-mail.

Price: Now only $550

PT3000 Laptop

Learn the exciting new Visions system!

Use your computer for everything — TV, movies, schoolwork, office work, Internet, phone!

More power and less energy.
Price: $2,600

I recommend the PB1000 Laptop.

It's _____ .

It's _____ .

It's _____ .

It's _____ .

It's _____ .

I recommend the PT3000 Laptop.

It's _____ .

It's _____ .

It's _____ .

It's _____ .

It's _____ .

Student's Name _____

Date _____

Reading an Ad

Read the refrigerator ad. Circle T for True or F for False.

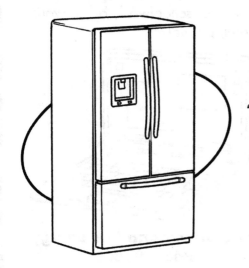

Keep Your Cool with Silver Line's New 3000 Refrigerator!

❋ Taller and wider than the 2000 so you can keep more food fresh!

❋ 3 doors make it easier to reach food!

❋ Same power as the 2000, but uses half the energy!

❋ Faster ice maker than the 2000!

❋ Cleaner water than the 2000 with its new five filter cleaning system!

"The Silver Line 3000 is quieter and more efficient than any other large refrigerator."
—*Electric Review*

Price: $2,600

1. The 2000 is as powerful as the 3000.   T   F

2. The 3000 is more energy-efficient than the 2000.   T   F

3. The 2000 has cleaner water than the 3000.   T   F

4. The 3000 is larger than the 2000.   T   F

5. The 3000 is easier-to-use than the 2000.   T   F

6. According to *Electric Review*, the Silver Line 3000 is quieter   T   F
   and more convenient than any other large refrigerator.

7. According to the ad, bigger is better.   T   F

Student's Name _____

Date _____

Clothing Labels

Look at the clothing labels. Circle T for True and F for False.

1. This clothing item is for men.   T   F

2. You should use only cold water to wash it.   T   F

3. You can use bleach.   T   F

4. You should hang the item to dry it.   T   F

5. You should iron it at a low temperature.   T   F

6. This clothing item is for women.   T   F

7. You should wash it in a machine.   T   F

8. You should wash it in hot water.   T   F

9. You can use bleach.   T   F

10. You should iron it at a high temperature.   T   F

11. This is children's clothing.   T   F

12. This is medium size.   T   F

13. You should wash it in a machine.   T   F

14. You should put it in a warm dryer.   T   F

15. You should dry clean it.   T   F

16. This size is extra-small.   T   F

17. You should use only cold water to wash it.   T   F

18. You should wash it by hand.   T   F

19. You should put it in a hot dryer.   T   F

20. You should dry clean it.   T   F

Student's Name _____

Date _____

Returning a Store Item

A. Put the conversation in order. Number the lines from 1 to 8.

_____ May I help you?

_____ What's the matter with them?

_____ Do you have your receipt?

_____ Would you like to exchange them?

_____ Yes. I'd like to return these pants.

_____ No, thank you. I'd like a refund, please.

_____ Yes. Here it is.

_____ They're too short.

**B. Look at the pictures and complete the conversations. Use these
    adjectives:** *large, long, short, and tight.*

1. A. What's the matter with the skirt?

   B. _____

2. A. What's the matter with the pants?

   B. _____

3. A. What's the matter with the jacket?

   B. _____

4. A. What's the matter with the shoes?

   B. _____

Using an ATM

A. Circle the correct answer.

1. I can't use an ATM if I forget my _____.

    a. PIN   b. account number   c. money

2. Which of the following is *not* a transaction?

    a. withdrawal   b. deposit   c. ATM

3. I want to find out how much money is in my account. Which button do I press?

    a. deposit   b. balance inquiry   c. fast cash

4. I want to put money into my account. Which button do I press?

    a. withdrawal   b. deposit   c. PIN

5. I want to take money out of my account. Which button do I press?

    a. transfer   b. deposit   c. withdrawal

6. I want to move money from one bank account to another bank account. Which button do I press?

    a. withdrawal   b. transfer   c. balance inquiry

B. Put the ATM instructions in the correct order from 1 to 6.

Taking Money out of an ATM

    _____ Take your card out of the machine.

    _____ Press the amount of money you want to take out.

    _____ Press the withdrawal button.

    _____ Put your card in the machine.

    _____ Enter your personal identification number.

    _____ Take your money and the receipt.

Reading and Writing a Check

A. Read the check and answer the questions.

```
┌──────────────────────────────────────────────────────────────────┐
│ Mei Ling                    BELMONT SAVINGS BANK            1103   │
│ 1217 Water Street                                                  │
│ Greenwood, FL 32443                    DATE  8/2/10                │
│                                                                    │
│ PAY TO THE    Southern Gas Company              $  76.04          │
│ ORDER OF                                                           │
│                         04                                         │
│     Seventy-six and    /100 _____ dollars     │
│                                                                    │
│ For   April bill #29530              Mei Ling                      │
└──────────────────────────────────────────────────────────────────┘
```

1. Who is the check from? _____

2. Who is the check to? _____

3. When did the person write the check? _____

4. How much is the check for? _____

B. Write these checks. Write today's date and sign your name.

Pay $45.10 to Community Telephone Company.

```
┌──────────────────────────────────────────────────────────────────┐
│                    CITYWIDE SAVINGS BANK                    101    │
│                                                                    │
│                                          DATE _____      │
│                                                                    │
│ PAY TO THE                                        $ _____       │
│ ORDER OF _____                  │
│                                                                    │
│ _____ dollars     │
│                                                                    │
│ For _____    _____            │
└──────────────────────────────────────────────────────────────────┘
```

Pay $76.50 to Gray's Department Store.

```
┌──────────────────────────────────────────────────────────────────┐
│                    CITYWIDE SAVINGS BANK                    102    │
│                                                                    │
│                                          DATE _____      │
│                                                                    │
│ PAY TO THE                                        $ _____       │
│ ORDER OF _____                  │
│                                                                    │
│ _____ dollars     │
│                                                                    │
│ For _____    _____            │
└──────────────────────────────────────────────────────────────────┘
```

Business Schedules

Look at the schedules. Complete the conversations.

Barber Shop			
Mon	CLOSED		
Tues	9:00	–	6:00
Wed	9:00	–	6:00
Thurs	9:00	–	7:00
Fri	9:00	–	7:00
Sat	8:00	–	6:00
Sun	CLOSED		

MUSEUM			
Monday	CLOSED		
Tuesday	CLOSED		
Wednesday	10:00	–	5:00
Thursday	10:00	–	7:00
Friday	10:00	–	5:00
Saturday	10:00	–	6:00
Sunday	12:00	–	5:00

Shopping Mall			
M	9:30	–	9:00
T	9:30	–	9:00
W	9:30	–	9:00
Th	9:30	–	9:00
F	9:30	–	10:00
S	9:00	–	10:00
S	12:00	–	6:00

1. A. What time does the museum open on Wednesday?

   B. It opens at _____.

2. A. What time does the mall open on Sunday?

   B. It opens at _____.

3. A. What days is the barber shop closed?

   B. It's closed on _____ and _____.

4. A. How many hours is the museum open on Thursday?

   B. It's open for _____ hours.

5. A. What days is the museum closed?

   B. It's closed on _____ and _____.

6. A. What time does the _____ open on Saturday?

   B. It opens at 8:00.

7. A. What time does the _____ close on Sunday?

   B. It closes at 5:00.

8. A. What time does the _____ close on Friday?

   B. It closes at 10:00.

Student's Name _____

Date _____

Reading a Train Schedule

Look at the schedule. Circle T for True or F for False.

	AM	PM	PM	PM	PM	PM	PM	PM
Kingston	11:15	1:15	3:15	4:15	5:01	5:45	6:15	7:03
Lancaster	11:23	1:23	3:23	4:23	5:09	5:53	6:23	7:11
Billings	11:31	1:31	3:31	4:31	5:17	6:01	6:31	7:19
Winchester	11:42	1:42	3:42	4:42	5:28	6:12	6:42	7:30
Medford	11:48	1:48	3:48	4:48	5:34	6:18	6:48	7:36
Central Station	11:59	1:59	3:59	4:59	5:45	6:29	6:59	7:47

1. It takes one hour to travel from Kingston to Central Station. T F

2. The morning train gets into Central Station at 7:47 AM. T F

3. You're on the 1:15 train. You'll get to Central Station at 1:59. T F

4. You need to meet someone at Central Station at 2:30. You should T F
   take the 1:23 train from Lancaster.

5. It's 6:10. The next train leaves Billings in 11 minutes. T F

6. It's 3:30. The next train leaves Medford at 4:48. T F

7. It's 12:00. The next train leaves Kingston in one hour and fifteen T F
   minutes.

8. You need to meet someone in Medford at 7:00. You should take T F
   the 6:15 train from Kingston.

9. It's 6:10. The next train leaves Winchester in twelve minutes. T F

10. It's a quarter to one in Billings. The next train is in 41 minutes. T F

Work Skills and a Job Application

A. What jobs are these people looking for? Read about their skills. Complete the sentences with the correct occupations. *Note:* Use each occupation *twice.*

an electrician	a mechanic	a medical technician

1. I'm looking for a job as _____. I can fix cars.

2. I'm looking for a job as _____. I can install light fixtures.

3. I'm looking for a job as _____. I can tune up engines.

4. I'm looking for a job as _____. I can do lab tests.

5. I'm looking for a job as _____. I can wire a house.

6. I'm looking for a job as _____. I can take blood samples.

B. Complete the job application.

Application for Employment

Name _____ **Social Security Number** _____

Address _____
STREET   CITY   STATE   ZIP CODE

Phone No. _____ **Age** (IF UNDER 21) _____ **Date of Birth** (IF UNDER 21) __ __ / __ __ / __ __ __ __

Position desired _____ **Total hours available** _____ **Date you can start** _____
PER WEEK

EDUCATION

Type of School	Name	Location	Years attended	Graduated?
High School				
College				
Other				

EMPLOYMENT

Date (Month/Year)	Employer (NAME & ADDRESS)	Position	Salary
From: To:			
From: To:			

Today's Date _____ **Signature** _____

Student's Name _____

Date _____

Requesting a Schedule Change

A. Put the conversation in the correct order.

_____ Could I possibly come in an hour late on Friday morning?

_____ Yes?

_____ Excuse me, Mrs. Jones.

_____ Thank you very much.

_____ An hour late?

_____ I understand. Yes. That'll be okay.

_____ Yes. The reason is I have to go to court.

B. Match the sentence beginnings with their endings.

_____ **1.** Could I possibly come in   **a.** to court.

_____ **2.** Could I possibly leave an   **b.** break now?

_____ **3.** Could I possibly take a   **c.** the doctor.

_____ **4.** Could I possibly take   **d.** an hour late?

_____ **5.** I have to go   **e.** a parent–teacher conference.

_____ **6.** I have   **f.** the day off?

_____ **7.** I have to take my mother to   **g.** hour early?

Help Wanted Ads

A. Write the full words next to the abbreviations.

evenings	hour	preferred
excellent	Monday to Friday	required
experience	month	week
full-time	part-time	years

1. hr. _____   **7.** req. _____

2. wk. _____   **8.** pref. _____

3. mo. _____   **9.** exp. _____

4. yrs. _____   **10.** excel. _____

5. M-F _____   **11.** FT _____

6. eves. _____   **12.** PT _____

B. Read the help wanted ads. Choose the correct answer.

FT Salespeople
2 yrs. exp. req. $1800-$2800/mo. Excel. benefits. Call Ms. Lima at (812) 595-2115.

PT Dishwasher Needed
Eves. M-F. $9/hr. Exp. pref. Apply in person. China Palace 229 Bow Street.

1. The salespeople have to _____.
a. send a resume
b. apply in person
c. have experience
d. work part-time

2. The salesperson ad has _____.
a. the name of the business
b. the name of the person to call
c. the work hours
d. the work days

3. The dishwasher has to _____.
a. send a resume
b. have experience
c. work full-time
d. apply in person

4. The ad for the dishwasher doesn't have _____.
a. the number of work hours
b. the name of the business
c. the pay
d. the work days

Reading a Pay Stub

Read the pay stub and answer the questions.

David Sanchez
PAY PERIOD
02/17/10 – 02/23/10

EARNINGS	RATE	HOURS	THIS PERIOD	YEAR TO DATE
REGULAR	12.00	40	480.00	3,360.00
OVERTIME	18.00	10	180.00	450.00
GROSS PAY			660.00	3,810.00
TAXES & DEDUCTIONS			THIS PERIOD	YEAR TO DATE
FEDERAL TAX			76.00	571.00
STATE TAX			20.00	114.00
FICA/MEDICARE			49.00	285.00
TOTAL			145.00	970.00
NET PAY			515.00	2,840.00

1. How many days are in this pay period? _____

2. What is David's regular rate of pay? _____

3. How many regular hours did David work this pay period? _____

4. How many overtime hours did he work this pay period? _____

5. How much money did David earn before taxes and deductions this pay period? _____

6. How much money did David's employer take out in taxes and deductions this pay period? _____

7. How much is David's paycheck for this pay period? _____

8. What are David's earnings so far in 2010? _____

Student's Name _____

Date _____

Reading an Accident Report

A. Read the accident report. Write T for True or F for False.

EMPLOYEE ACCIDENT REPORT

Name of injured employee: __Hassan Ali__   SS#: __222-40-6718__ Sex: __✓__ M ___ F

Job Title: __Electrician__   Department: __Maintenance__   Date of Report: __4/02/10__

Where did accident occur? __Cafeteria kitchen__   Date of Accident: __3/28/10__

Time of Accident: __6:00__ (A.M.)/P.M. Name(s) of Witness(es): __Paula Spellman__

Nature of injury and part(s) of body injured: __I got a shock in my hand.__

How did the employee get injured? __I was installing a dishwasher. I touched a "live" wire.__

What safety equipment, if any, did employee use? __boots__

What factors contributed to the accident? __There wasn't enough light. I couldn't see the__ __wires very well.__

Did employee lose time from work? __Yes__   How much time? __One day__

Immediate Supervisor signature: __Sammy Tate__   Date signed: __4/02/10__

____ **1.** Hassan is a technician.

____ **2.** The accident was in the evening.

____ **3.** Hassan touched a wrong wire and got a shock.

____ **4.** Nobody saw the accident.

____ **5.** Hassan missed one day of work because of the accident.

B. Imagine an accident at work. Complete the accident report form.

EMPLOYEE ACCIDENT REPORT

Name of injured employee: _____ SS#: _____ Sex: ___ M ___ F

Home address of employee: _____ Date of Birth: _____

Job Title: _____ Department: _____ Date of Report: _____

Where did accident occur? _____ Date of Accident: _____

Time of Accident: _____ A.M./P.M. Name(s) of Witness(es): _____

Nature of injury and part(s) of body injured: _____

How did the employee get injured? _____

What safety equipment, if any, did employee use? _____

What factors contributed to the accident? _____

Did employee lose time from work? _____ How much time? _____

Immediate Supervisor signature: _____ Date signed: _____

Student's Name _____

Date _____

Emergencies at Home

A. Complete the sentences.

_____ **1.** My mother is having   **a.** on medicine!

_____ **2.** My daughter overdosed   **b.** a heart attack!

_____ **3.** My sister isn't   **c.** a gun!

_____ **4.** Someone is breaking   **d.** a fire!

_____ **5.** There's a dangerous person with   **e.** into our house!

_____ **6.** There's a lot of smoke. I think there's   **f.** breathing!

B. Complete the paragraph with the correct words.

dial 911	fire extinguisher	smoke detectors
emergency numbers	first-aid kit	utilities

My family is prepared for an emergency at home. There's a list of

_____¹ next to the kitchen phone. If anyone gets

hurt, there's a _____² in the bathroom. If there's a fire in the

kitchen, we have a _____³ there. Also, I make sure all

our _____⁴ work. I change their batteries twice a year. My

husband and I know how to turn off the _____⁵ in the basement. And

everyone in my home knows how to _____⁶ if we need an ambulance,

police car, or fire truck.

First Aid

A. What's the emergency? Write the medical emergency for each first-aid instruction below.

| Animal Bites | Bee Stings | Bleeding | Burns | Choking | Electric Shock |

1. _____: Put the wound in cool water for 5 minutes.

2. _____: Don't touch the person.

3. _____: Put ice on the wound.

4. _____: Perform the Heimlich maneuver.

5. _____: Wash the wound for five minutes.

6. _____: Apply pressure to the wound for ten minutes.

B. Look at the first-aid kit. Find the items in the list below. Write the correct letter next to each item.

_____ **1.** adhesive tape   _____ **5.** elastic bandage   _____ **8.** scissors

_____ **2.** antibiotic ointment _____ **6.** hydrogen peroxide   _____ **9.** tweezers

_____ **3.** antiseptic wipe   _____ **7.** pain reliever   _____ **10.** sterile dressing

_____ **4.** bandages   pad

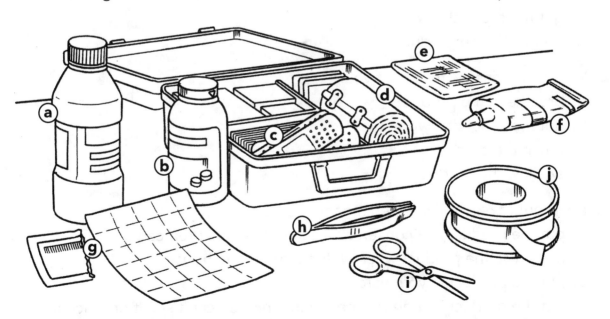

Student's Name _____

Date _____

Reading a Warning Label

A. Complete the warning label with the following words.

breathe	harmful	skin
call	medical	soap
drink	reach	water

▼ DANGER ▼

Avoid contact with _____ [1] or eyes. _____ [2] if swallowed. Do not _____ [3] vapors.

▼ FIRST-AID TREATMENT ▼

• If swallowed: _____ [4] a glass of water or milk. _____ [5] a Poison Control Center.

• If in eyes: Rinse with _____ [6] for 15 minutes. Get _____ [7] attention.

• If on skin: Wash thoroughly with _____ [8] and water. • Keep out of _____ [9] of children.

B. Read the above label again and answer the questions.

1. You should call the Poison Control Center if you _____.
   a. touch the product
   b. swallow the product
   c. get the product in your eyes
   d. breathe in the product

2. You should rinse with soap if you _____.
   a. breathe in the product
   b. get the product in your eyes
   c. touch the product
   d. swallow the product

3. *Keep out of reach of children* means _____.
   a. put the product in a convenient place where children can get it
   b. never use the product when children are in the house
   c. put the product in your yard
   d. put the product in a place where your children can't see it or touch it

Safety Procedures

Read the safety procedures again on student text page 92c. Check (✓) Yes or No for each statement.

In an Earthquake	Yes	No
1. If you are inside, stand close to heavy objects, like bookcases.	___	___
2. If you are inside, get under a table or desk.	___	___
3. If you are inside, turn towards the window.	___	___
4. Cover your head and your eyes.	___	___
5. If you are outside, stand close to electrical wires or poles.	___	___
6. If you are outside, go to an area with buildings.	___	___
7. If you are near a building, get down on your knees in a doorway.	___	___
8. If you are in a hall, keep your face up.	___	___

In a Hurricane	Yes	No
1. Have a plan to leave your home quickly.	___	___
2. Move trash cans, bicycles, and grills outside.	___	___
3. Put flashlights, medicine, and bottled water in your emergency kit.	___	___
4. Put food from your refrigerator in your emergency kit.	___	___
5. Turn off your TV and radio.	___	___
6. Fill your sink and bathtub with water for washing.	___	___
7. Open all your windows and doors.	___	___

Student's Name _____

Date _____

Renting an Apartment

A. Complete the conversation with the following words. (There is one extra word.)

allowed	deposit	parking	require
apartment	included	public transportation	utilities
available	month	rent	

A. I'm looking for a one-bedroom apartment.

B. We have a one-bedroom apartment _____[1].

A. Great. How much is the _____[2]?

B. It's $1050 a _____[3].

A. Does that include _____[4]?

B. Yes, it does. Water, gas, and electricity are _____[5].

A. Is there a security _____[6]?

B. Yes. We require two months' rent as a deposit.

A. Are pets _____[7]?

B. No, they aren't.

A. Is _____[8] included in the rent?

B. Yes. There's a space for one car.

A. Is there _____[9] nearby?

B. Yes. There's a bus stop a few blocks away.

   Would you like to see the _____[10]?

A. Yes, please.

B. Write the words on the correct line. You can use some words twice.

bathtub	dishwasher	light	sink	stove	toilet

1. Things that get clogged: _____

2. Things that leak: _____

3. Things that don't turn on: _____

Student's Name _____

Date _____

Reading Apartment Ads

Look at the apartment ads. Read the sentences. Write the letter of the apartment next to each sentence.

A
ESSEX Lg. apt. avail. now. 3 BR, 1.5 BA, liv.rm., mod. eat-in-kit., new refrig., d/w, washer & dryer. $1600 plus util. No pets. Call supt. 312–555–1629

B
MIDDLETON Sunny 1-BR apt. 1 BA, balc., 4th flr. Elev. in bldg., a/c, laundry rm. in bsmt. Pkg. No pets. $850. Util. incl. Call mgr. 312–555–0295

C
CENTERVILLE Beaut. 2-BR, 1 BA apt. in 2-fam. hse. Lge. kit., liv rm., din rm., nr. bus stop. Pets OK. $1200. Util. incl. Call owner. 971–555–1352

_____ **1.** It has three bedrooms

_____ **2.** Pets are allowed.

_____ **3.** Utilities are not included.

_____ **4.** It has a laundry room in the basement.

_____ **5.** Call the superintendent to find out more.

_____ **6.** It has parking.

_____ **7.** It's in a two-family house.

_____ **8.** Call the manager to find out more.

_____ **9.** It has one and a half bathrooms.

_____ **10.** It has air conditioning.

_____ **11.** It's near public transportation.

_____ **12.** There's a dishwasher in the kitchen.

_____ **13.** There's an elevator in the building.

_____ **14.** It has a new refrigerator.

Student's Name _____

Date _____

Rules and Regulations Checklist

Read *Building Rules and Regulations* **on student text page 102c again. Check**
(✓) Yes (*follows the rule*) or No (*doesn't follow the rule*) for each statement.

		Yes	No
1.	Pay your rent with cash.	____	____
2.	You can have a dance party until 1:00 in the morning.	____	____
3.	Keep hallways and stairs clear.	____	____
4.	Lock the door to your apartment whenever you leave.	____	____
5.	Give guests the key to your apartment.	____	____
6.	Tell the apartment manager if your apartment will be empty for a week.	____	____
7.	Disconnect your bathroom fan and smoke detectors.	____	____
8.	Tell the apartment manager when there is a problem with your smoke detector.	____	____
9.	Take your laundry out of the machine promptly.	____	____
10.	The laundry room is for you and your friends to use.	____	____
11.	Store bicycles and other personal belongings on your balcony.	____	____
12.	Keep your pet in your apartment.	____	____
13.	Park on the driveway.	____	____
14.	Talk to the landlord before you install a satellite dish.	____	____
15.	Use large nails to hang pictures on the apartment walls.	____	____

Student's Name _____

Date _____

Parts of the Face and Body

A. Write the correct word on each line.

cheek	eye	forehead	lip	teeth
chin	eyebrow	jaw	nose	tongue

1. _____

2. _____

3. _____

4. _____

5. _____

6. _____

7. _____

8. _____

9. _____

10. _____

B. Write the correct word on each line.

ankle	elbow	hand	knee	throat
arm	finger	head	neck	toe
chest	foot	hip	shoulder	wrist

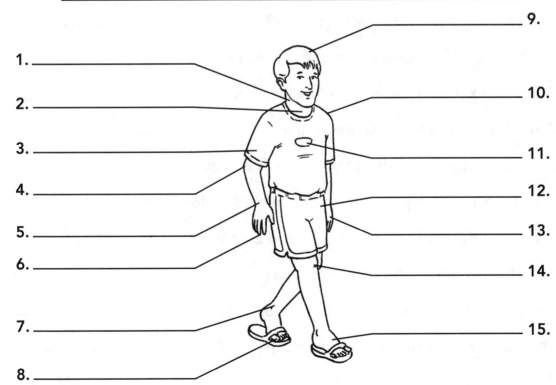

1. _____

2. _____

3. _____

4. _____

5. _____

6. _____

7. _____

8. _____

9. _____

10. _____

11. _____

12. _____

13. _____

14. _____

15. _____

Student's Name _____

Date _____

Reading Medicine Labels

Look at the medicine labels and answer the questions.

Breathe Clear Decongestant

DIRECTIONS: Take 2 capsules every six hours.
WARNING: Do not operate equipment while taking this medicine. It may make you drowsy.

TYLER ANTACID TABLETS

Dosage: two to four tablets as needed
Warning: Do not take more than 16 tablets in 24 hours.
Expiration Date: 03/11

Allergy-Free Antihistamine

Directions:
Take one tablet every four hours.
Warning:
Do not take more than six tablets in 24 hours.
Use before 08/12

ADDISON PAIN MEDICINE

Directions: Take 2 pills every six hours.
Warning: Stop use and see a doctor if you don't feel better in seven days.
Side effects: May upset stomach.

1. What's the dosage of the decongestant? _____

2. What are the side effects of the pain medicine? _____

3. What's the expiration date of the antihistamine? _____

4. What's the dosage of the antihistamine? _____

5. How many antacid tablets can you take in 24 hours? _____

6. What is the last date you can use the antacid tablets? _____

7. How much antihistamine can you take in 24 hours? _____

8. What's the dosage of the pain medicine? _____

9. What are the side effects of the decongestant? _____

10. Is the pain medicine a prescription drug? _____

Student's Name _____

Date _____

Nutrition; Medical History Form

A. Write the following foods and nutrients in the correct categories.

beans	cereal	fish	low-fat milk	mayonnaise	rice
calcium	desserts	fried foods	low-fat yogurt	potassium	soda

Protein	**Dairy**	**Grains**
_____	_____	_____
_____	_____	_____
Sugar	**Bad Fats**	**Minerals**
_____	_____	_____
_____	_____	_____

B. Complete the medical history form.

——————— *Midtown Medical Associates* ———————

Patient Information Form

Name _____ __ __/__ __/__ __
         FIRST   MIDDLE   LAST   DATE OF BIRTH

Address _____
         NUMBER   STREET   CITY   STATE   ZIP CODE

Daytime Phone _____ Evening Phone _____ Cell _____

Emergency Contact: Name _____ Relationship _____

               Phone _____

Height _____ Weight _____

Check any conditions or diseases you have:
____ allergies   ____ cancer   ____ heart disease   ____ kidney disease
____ asthma   ____ diabetes   ____ high blood pressure

Check any symptoms you have:
____ bad cough   ____ depression   ____ headaches   ____ bleeding easily   ____ trouble sleeping
____ chest pains   ____ fainting   ____ nausea   ____ trouble eating

If you checked any items above, please explain: _____

What medications do you take? _____

Student's Name _____

Date _____

A Telephone Bill

Look at the telephone bill and circle the correct answers.

Peter Wong
123 Jefferson Road
Medfield, MA 02052

Account Number: 2354768829
Phone Number: 508-555-2834
Billing Period: 10/04/10–11/03/10
Billing Date: 11/04/10

ACCOUNT SUMMARY			
Amount of Last Bill	$39.50	Current Charges	
Payment Thank You	39.50	Local Monthly Charges	$ 33.25
Balance	$ 0.00	Long Distance Service Charges	16.06
		Amount due on 11/22/10	$ 49.31

LOCAL TELEPHONE SERVICE			
Local Unlimited Calling	$ 22.00	Federal Tax	$ 0.62
Line Charge	6.50	State and Local Surcharge	0.32
Federal Tax	2.25	Single Bill Fee	2.35
State and Local Taxes	2.50	Long Distance Calls	12.77
Total Local Charges	$ 33.25	Total Long Distance Charges	$ 16.06

LONG DISTANCE SERVICE						
DATE	TIME	PLACE AND NUMBER CALLED	TYPE	RATE	MINUTES	AMOUNT
10/04/10	7:05 P.M.	LA, CA (213) 555-1769	Direct	Night	12	1.20
10/11/10	11:12 A.M.	NYC, NY (212) 555-9573	Direct	Day	2	0.50
10/12/10	5:48 P.M.	Dallas, TX (972) 222-8609	Direct	Day	18	4.50
10/28/10	12:28 P.M.	Phil, PA (445) 222-9678	Direct	Day	31	2.79
11/02/10	9:51 P.M.	Miami, FL (305) 444-2781	Direct	Night	42	3.78

1. What is Peter Wong's account number?
   a. 2354768829
   b. 508-555-2834
   c. 02052

2. How long is the billing period?
   a. a week
   b. two weeks
   c. a month

3. When is this bill due?
   a. 10/04/10
   b. 11/04/10
   c. 11/22/10

4. How much was Peter's last phone bill?
   a. $22.00
   b. $39.50
   c. $6.50

5. How much is this phone bill?
   a. $16.06
   b. $33.25
   c. $49.31

6. How much are the long distance charges?
   a. $16.06
   b. $33.25
   c. $49.31

7. How many long distance phone calls did Peter make between 10/04 and 11/03?
   a. 4
   b. 5
   c. 6

Telephone Directory

Choose the correct answer.

			RIV–ROF	528
RIVER	**Tom** 200 Plain View Cla	....	**517–593–9827**	
	Victor 2925 Washington Av Gre	....	**231–257–6821**	
RIVERA	**A & J** 780 Central Cli	....	**517–897–0081**	
	Dennis 30 Broad Arc	....	**231–257–1171**	
	Teresa 175 Federal Can	....	**734–545–9338**	
RIVES	**D** 32 Grant Cla	....	**517–593–2451**	
RIVKIN	**Natalie** 32 Pine Arc	....	**231–257–2451**	
RIZZO	**Anthony** 1480 Main She	....	**517–593–2451**	
	C & E 1770 Oak Roc	....	**734–545–0095**	

1. Alice and Jake Rivera live in _____.

    a. Clayton   c. Clinton

    b. Canton   d. Greenville

2. The area code for Rockwood is _____.

    a. 743   c. 231

    b. 517   d. 734

3. The phone number for _____ is on a different page.

    a. Liz Roach   c. Joan Rodriquez

    b. Bill Rogers   d. William Robson

4. Natalie Rivkin lives in _____.

    a. Arcadia   c. Redford

    b. Canton   d. Clayton

5. Charles and Ellen Rizzo live on _____.

    a. Main Street   c. Oak Street

    b. Federal Street   d. Plain View Avenue

6. Victor River's phone number is _____.

    a. 231-275-6821   c. 517-593-9827

    b. 517-897-0081   d. 231-257-6821

Reading the Yellow Pages

Circle T for True or F for False.

BAGELS
Bagel Land
  21 Davis Avenue, Fairfield .... (352) 889–1327
Bob's Bagels – see our ad this page
  24 High Street, Melrose .... (352) 298–9911

BAGS
The Packaging Store
  52 Medford Way, Webster .... (352) 298–4545

BAKERIES
Cake Walk
  167 Common Avenue, Fairfield .... (352) 298–6162
Dolly's Donuts – see our ad this page
  52 Lakeview Road, Webster .... (352) 298–5067
Whole Desserts – see our ad this page
  21 Lewiston Ave, Melrose .... (352) 889–6590

Bob's Bagels

The freshest in town!
Try our new raisin nut bagel.

Open 5:00 AM – 3:00 PM every day
We also serve Coffee, Soup, & Sandwiches
24 High Street, Melrose (352) 298–9911

**Fried fresh
for you!**

Open 24 hours!
"The best donuts in town!"

52 Lakeview Road, Webster (352) 298–5067

 WHOLE DESSERTS
WHOLE WHEAT BREAD, FRUIT CAKE
WHOLE GRAIN COOKIES, LOW-FAT APPLE CAKE

6:00 AM – 4:00 PM MONDAY – SATURDAY
21 LEWISTON AVE MELROSE 352 889–6590

---

1. Dolly's Donuts is open at 3:00 in the morning.   T   F

2. Whole Desserts is open every day.   T   F

3. The phone number for The Packaging Store is 325–298–4545.   T   F

4. The address of the bagel store in Melrose is 21 Davis Avenue.   T   F

5. Dolly's Donuts is in Webster.   T   F

6. Bob's Bagels serves lunch.   T   F

7. Whole Desserts sells donuts.   T   F

8. The phone number for the bakery in Fairfield is 352–298–6590.   T   F

Requesting Apartment Maintenance or Repairs

A. Complete the conversation with the following words. (There is one extra word.)

apartment	help	tell
called	running	toilet
checks	stove	

A. Hello. This is Jin-Hee Lee in _____¹ 5D.

B. Yes. How can I _____² you?

A. I _____³ a few days ago. My _____⁴ is broken.

B. I'm sorry. Please _____⁵ me the problem again.

A. The water keeps _____⁶.

B. Okay. I'll make sure someone _____⁷ your toilet today.

A. Thank you very much.

B. Complete the conversation with the following words. (There is one extra word.)

broken	flush	light	stuck
drips	leaks	open	turn

1. The toilet doesn't _____.

2. The burners on the stove don't _____.

3. The key gets _____ in the lock.

4. The window won't _____.

5. The bathtub faucet _____.

6. The heat is _____.

7. The lights don't _____ on.

Reading a Rental Agreement

Read the rental agreement. Circle T for True or F for False.

Rental Agreement

THIS AGREEMENT IS BETWEEN:

_____ **Carlos Mesa** _____ as LANDLORD and _____ **Alison Worth** _____ as TENANT.
The LANDLORD leases to the TENANT apartment number : **2A** at **115 Broadway** Fairmont,
Maine 04263 for the term of _____ **twelve months** _____ beginning **September 1, 2012** and
ending on _____ **August 31, 2013** _____ .

TERMS AND CONDITIONS OF THIS AGREEMENT:

1. **RENT:** The total rent for the apartment is _____ **$9,000.00** _____ . The monthly rent is **$750.00**
   due on or before the _____ **first** _____ day of each month.

2. **UTILITIES AND SERVICES:** The TENANT will pay the following utility and service charges:
   _____ **Electricity, Telephone, and Internet** _____
   The LANDLORD will pay the following utility and service charges:
   _____ **Gas and Water** _____

3. **APPLIANCES:** The apartment is rented with the following appliances:
   _____ **Refrigerator and Dishwasher** _____
   The LANDLORD will repair appliances that the LANDLORD owns. The TENANT is responsible for
   repairing any other appliances.

4. **SECURITY DEPOSIT:** The TENANT will deposit with the LANDLORD a security deposit of
   _____ **$1,500.00** _____ . If the apartment is in good condition when the TENANT moves out, and all rent
   is paid, the LANDLORD will return the full amount of the security deposit within 30 days.

5. **ENTRY TO APARTMENT:** The LANDLORD has the right to enter the apartment if the
   LANDLORD gives 24-hour notice.

6. **CONDITION OF APARTMENT:** The TENANT agrees to take good care of the apartment. When
   the agreement ends, the TENANT will return the apartment in good clean condition.

---

1. The security deposit is two months' rent.   T   F

2. The tenant pays for gas and electricity.   T   F

3. The landlord will repair the dishwasher.   T   F

4. The landlord can come into the apartment if he calls first.   T   F

5. The rent is $9,000 a month.   T   F

6. When the agreement ends, the tenant must leave the apartment   T   F
   clean and in good condition.

Rights and Responsibilities

Read *Know Your Rights* **on student text page 136c again. Circle the correct word in the following sentences.**

1. The (landlord   tenant) has to provide an apartment with heating, plumbing, and electricity in working condition.

2. The (landlord   tenant) must keep the building and the land around it clean.

3. The (landlord   tenant) must keep the apartment clean.

4. The (landlord   tenant) must tell the (landlord   tenant) if a repair is needed.

5. The (landlord   tenant) can deduct the cost of the repair from the rent.

6. The (landlord   tenant) must make sure all locks on windows and doors work.

7. The (landlord   tenant) can evict a (landlord   tenant) if he or she doesn't pay the rent or breaks the rules and regulations of the building.

8. The (landlord   tenant) can use the security deposit to clean the apartment or make repairs.

9. The (landlord   tenant) can take the (landlord   tenant) to court if the (landlord   tenant) doesn't return the right amount of the security deposit.

10. The (landlord   tenant) cannot turn off the heat or electricity.

11. The (landlord   tenant) has to fix problems that make the apartment unhealthy and unsafe.

12. The (landlord   tenant) can take the (landlord   tenant) to court if the (landlord   tenant) doesn't pay the rent or follow the rules and regulations of the building.

Side by Side Plus 2
Life Skills Worksheet Answer Key

UNIT 1

Worksheet 1:
Dates and Forms
A.
1. Wednesday
2. Monday
3. Saturday
4. Tuesday
5. Friday
6. Thursday
7. Sunday
8. March
9. October
10. January
11. May
12. November
13. February
14. July
15. August
16. December
17. June
18. April
19. September

B.
1. 01/08/09
2. 07/10/10
3. 03/12/08
4. 05/03/06
5. 09/05/07
6. 11/30/12
7. 04/09/11
8. 02/22/09
9. 08/01/81
10. 10/02/08
11. 12/06/10
12. 06/04/97

C.
(Answers will vary.)

Worksheet 2:
Reading a Community Calendar
A.
1. T   4. F
2. F   5. T
3. F   6. F

B.
1. (Circle October 21.)
2. (Circle October 27.)
3. (Circle October 31.)
4. (Circle October 12.)
5. (Circle October 2, 9, 16, 23, 30.)
6. (Circle October 18.)

Worksheet 3:
The American Education System
A.
1. b
2. d
3. a
4. c
5. g
6. h
7. e
8. f

B.
6
3
1
2
4
5

UNIT 2

Worksheet 4:
School Personnel & Locations
A.
1. nurse's office
2. gym
3. library
4. cafeteria
5. hall
6. school office
7. guidance office
8. principal's office
9. auditorium

B.
1. h
2. e
3. f
4. d
5. a
6. g
7. c
8. b

Worksheet 5:
Reading a School Floor Plan
1. T   6. T
2. F   7. F
3. F   8. T
4. T   9. T
5. T   10. F

Worksheet 6:
Parts of a Computer
1. f
2. k
3. i
4. b
5. a
6. l
7. d
8. c
9. e
10. j
11. g
12. h

UNIT 3
Worksheet 7:
Locating Items in a Supermarket
1. Produce, 6
2. Dairy, 1
3. Beverages, 3
4. Baked Goods, 2
5. Frozen Foods, 4
6. Baked Goods, 2
7. Meat, 5
8. Produce, 6

Worksheet 8:
Counting U.S. Currency; Reading a Receipt
A.
1. 27¢ $.27
2. 36¢ $.36
3. $3.05
4. $15.10
5. $40.50
6. $5.26

B.
1. $2.99
2. $1.99
3. $4.50
4. $.25
5. $3.00
6. gallon, quart
7. $24.94

Worksheet 9:
Reading a Food Label
1. a
2. b
3. b
4. c
5. b
6. a

Worksheet 10:
Units of Measure for Food
A.
1. fluid ounce
2. teaspoon
3. cup
4. tablespoon
5. gallon
6. quart
7. pint
8. pound

B.
4
2
3
7
5
1
6

C.
gallon
gallon
pint
quart
pound

UNIT 4
Worksheet 11:
Offers and Invitations
1. a
2. c
3. b
4. c
5. a
6. b

Worksheet 12:
Reading Invitations
1. F   5. T
2. F   6. F
3. F   7. F
4. T   8. T

UNIT 5
Worksheet 13:
Comparing Computers
(Answers will vary.)

Worksheet 14:
Reading an Ad
1. T   5. T
2. T   6. F
3. F   7. T
4. T

UNIT 6

Worksheet 15:
Clothing Labels

1. T	11. T
2. T	12. T
3. F	13. F
4. F	14. F
5. T	15. F
6. T	16. F
7. T	17. F
8. F	18. F
9. T	19. F
10. T	20. T

Worksheet 16:
Returning a Store Item
A.

```
   1
   3
   7
   5
   2
   6
   8
   4
```

B.
1. It's too long.
2. They're too short.
3. It's too large.
4. They're too tight.

Worksheet 17:
Using an ATM
A.
1. a
2. c
3. b
4. b
5. c
6. b

B.

```
   6
   4
   3
   1
   2
   5
```

Worksheet 18:
Reading and Writing a Check
A.
1. Mei Ling
2. Southern Gas Company
3. August 2, 2010
4. $76.04

B.
(Students should enter current date and sign the checks.)

Community Telephone Company $45.10
Forty-five and 10/100

Gray's Department Store $76.50
Seventy-six and 50/100

UNIT 7

Worksheet 19:
Business Schedules
1. 10:00
2. 12:00
3. Monday, Sunday
4. 9
5. Monday, Tuesday
6. barber shop
7. museum
8. shopping mall

Worksheet 20:
Reading a Train Schedule

1. F	6. F
2. F	7. T
3. T	8. T
4. T	9. F
5. F	10. F

UNIT 8

Worksheet 21:
Work Skills and a Job Application
A.
1. a mechanic
2. an electrician
3. a mechanic
4. a medical technician
5. an electrician
6. a medical technician

B.
(Answers will vary.)

Worksheet 22:
Requesting a Schedule Change
A.

```
   3
   2
   1
   7
   4
   6
   5
```

B.
1. d
2. g
3. b

4. f
5. a
6. e
7. c

Worksheet 23:
Help Wanted Signs
A.
1. hour
2. week
3. month
4. years
5. Monday to Friday
6. evenings
7. required
8. preferred
9. experience
10. excellent
11. full-time
12. part-time

B.
1. c
2. b
3. d
4. a

Worksheet 24:
Reading a Pay Stub
1. 7
2. $12.00 an hour
3. 40
4. 10
5. $660
6. $145
7. $515.00
8. $2,840.00

Worksheet 25:
Reading an Accident Report
A.
1. F   4. F
2. F   5. T
3. T

B.
(Answers will vary.)

UNIT 9
Worksheet 26:
Emergencies at Home
A.
1. b
2. a
3. f
4. e
5. c
6. d

B.
1. emergency numbers
2. first-aid kit
3. fire extinguisher
4. smoke detectors
5. utilities
6. dial 911

Worksheet 27:
First Aid
A.
1. Burns
2. Electric Shock
3. Bee Stings
4. Choking
5. Animal Bites
6. Bleeding

B.
1. j
2. f
3. g
4. c
5. d
6. a
7. b
8. i
9. h
10. e

Worksheet 28:
Reading a Warning Label
A.
1. skin
2. Harmful
3. breathe
4. drink
5. Call
6. water
7. medical
8. soap
9. reach

B.
1. b
2. b
3. d

Worksheet 29:
Safety Procedures
In an Earthquake

	Yes	No
1.		✓
2.	✓	
3.		✓
4.	✓	
5.		✓
6.		✓

7. ✓   —
8. —   ✓

In a Hurricane

	Yes	No
1.	✓	—
2.	—	✓
3.	✓	—
4.	—	✓
5.	—	✓
6.	✓	—
7.	—	✓

5.	—	✓
6.	✓	—
7.	—	✓
8.	✓	—
9.	✓	—
10.	—	✓
11.	—	✓
12.	—	✓
13.	—	✓
14.	✓	—
15.	—	✓

UNIT 10

Worksheet 30:
Renting an Apartment
A.
1. available
2. rent
3. month
4. utilities
5. included
6. deposit
7. allowed
8. parking
9. public transportation
10. apartment

B.
1. bathtub, sink, toilet
2. bathtub, dishwasher, sink, toilet
3. dishwasher, light, stove

Worksheet 31:
Reading Apartment Ads
A.
1. A
2. C
3. A
4. B
5. A
6. B
7. C
8. B
9. A
10. B
11. C
12. A
13. B
14. A

Worksheet 32:
Rules and Regulations Checklist

	Yes	No
1.	—	✓
2.	—	✓
3.	✓	—
4.	✓	—

UNIT 11

Worksheet 33:
Parts of the Body and Face
A.
1. forehead
2. eye
3. cheek
4. jaw
5. tongue
6. eyebrow
7. nose
8. lip
9. teeth
10. chin

B.
1. neck
2. throat
3. arm
4. elbow
5. wrist
6. finger
7. ankle
8. toe
9. head
10. shoulder
11. chest
12. hip
13. hand
14. knee
15. foot

Worksheet 34:
Reading Medicine Labels
1. 2 capsules every 6 hours
2. It may upset your stomach.
3. 08/12
4. one tablet every four hours
5. 16
6. 03/11
7. 6 tablets
8. 2 pills every six hours
9. It may make you drowsy.
10. No

Worksheet 35:
Nutrition; Medical History Form
A.

Protein	**Dairy**	**Grains**
beans	low-fat milk	cereal
fish	low-fat yogurt	rice

Sugar	**Bad Fats**	**Minerals**
desserts	fried foods	calcium
soda	mayonnaise	potassium

B.
(Answers will vary.)

UNIT 12

Worksheet 36:
A Telephone Bill
1. a
2. c
3. c
4. b
5. c
6. a
7. b

Worksheet 37:
Telephone Directory
1. c
2. d
3. b
4. a
5. c
6. d

Worksheet 38:
Reading the Yellow Pages
1. T   5. T
2. F   6. T
3. F   7. F
4. F   8. F

UNIT 13

Worksheet 39:
Requesting Apartment Maintenance or Repairs
A.
1. apartment
2. help
3. called
4. toilet
5. tell
6. running
7. checks

B.
1. flush
2. light
3. stuck
4. open
5. drips
6. broken
7. turn

Worksheet 40:
Reading a Rental Agreement
1. T   4. T
2. F   5. F
3. T   6. T

Worksheet 41:
Rights and Responsibilities
1. landlord
2. landlord
3. tenant
4. tenant, landlord
5. tenant
6. landlord
7. landlord, tenant
8. landlord
9. tenant, landlord, landlord
10. landlord
11. landlord
12. landlord, tenant, tenant

Side by Side Plus 2
Activity Masters

The activity masters include ready-to-use word cards, graphics, charts, and activity sheets for the multilevel activities and games suggested throughout the *Side by Side Plus 2* Teacher's Guide.

Unit 1
1 Student Interview
2 Birthday Survey
3 Information Gap: *Calendars*
4 What's the Story?
5 Concentration: *Months of the Year*
6 Concentration: *Irregular Past Tense Verbs*
7 Verb Form Review
8 Unit 1 Board Game

Unit 2
9 Match Game: *School Personnel & Locations*
10 Information Gap: *Madison High School*
11 Sequencing Instructions: *Setting up a Computer*
12 Scrambled Sentence Prompts
13 Food Concentration Cards: *Fruits & Vegetables*
14 Match Game: *Questions & Answers*
15 Unit 2 Board Game

Unit 3
16 Match Game: *In the Supermarket*
17 Information Gap: *Supermarket Receipts*
18 Sense or Nonsense?

Unit 4
19 Information Gap: *An Invitation*
20 Graphic Organizer: *Being a Guest for Dinner*
21 Pair Interview: *What's Polite in Your Country?*
22 Miming Game Word Cards
23 Time Capsule!

Unit 5
24 Electronics and Appliance Word Cards
25 Graphic Organizer: *Letters to the Editor*
26 Comparisons: *Then and Now*
27 Match Game: *Nouns and Adjectives*

Unit 6
28 Match Game: *Questions and Answers*
29 Information Gap: *Checks*
30 Gray's Department Store: *Applying the Rules*
31 Adjective Word Cards
32 Payment and Banking Bingo

Unit 7
33 Information Gap: *Business Schedules*
34 Concentration: *Traffic Signs*
35 Information Gap: *Transportation Schedules*
36 Safe Driving Checklist
37 Sense or Nonsense: *Safe Driving*
38 Places Around Town Word Cards
39 Survey: *How Do You Get to School?*

Unit 8
40 Find the Right Person!
41 Concentration: *Help Wanted Ad Abbreviations*
42 Matching Want Ads
43 Pay Stub Bingo
44 Information Gap: *Pay Stub*
45 Find the Synonyms!
46 Tic Tac Adverbs

Unit 9
47 Survey: *Are You Prepared for Emergencies?*
48 First-Aid Bingo
49 Miming Game: *Emergency Procedures*
50 Verb Miming Game
51 Scrambled Sentences
52 Match Game: *First Aid and Emergency Responses*
53 Unit 9 Board Game

Unit 10
54 Match Game: *Apartment Rentals*
55 Information Gap: *Renting an Apartment*

56 Concentration: *Apartment Ad Abbreviations I*
57 Concentration: *Apartment Ad Abbreviations II*
58 Matching Apartment Ads
59 Tic Tac Adjectives

Unit 11
60 Role Play: *Telephone Calls*
61 Medicine Bingo
62 Medicine Quiz
63 Miming Game: *A Medical Checkup*
64 Food Word Cards
65 Match Game: *Good Advice*
66 Health Information Quiz

Unit 12
67 Information Gap: *Taking Messages*
68 Match Game: *Who Do I Call?*
69 Class Directory Survey
70 Our Class Directory
71 Business Name Cards
72 Survey: *What Kind of Phone Do You Use?*
73 Discussion: *Advantages and Disadvantages*

Unit 13
74 Interview: *Household Solutions*
75 Sequence the Story: *A Clogged Sink*
76 Unit 13 Board Game

A. Complete the form with your own information.*

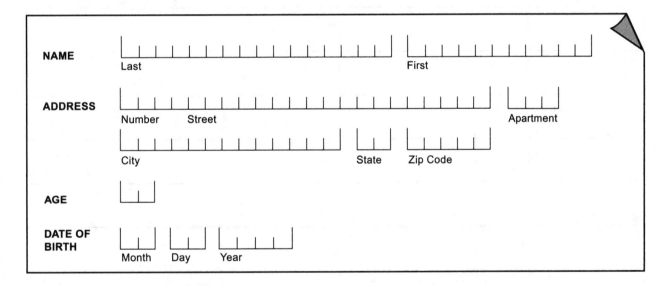

NAME	Last First
ADDRESS	Number Street Apartment
	City State Zip Code
AGE	
DATE OF BIRTH	Month Day Year

*Or you can make up any information you wish.

B. Interview your partner. Write your partner's information on the form.

NAME	Last First
ADDRESS	Number Street Apartment
	City State Zip Code
AGE	
DATE OF BIRTH	Month Day Year

What's your last name?
What's your first name?
How do you spell that?
What's your address?

What's your zip code?
How old are you?
What's your date of birth?

Name	Birthday

When is your birthday?
How do you spell your name?

Calendar A

September						
S	M	T	W	Th	F	S
				1	2	3 Dance Party
4	5	6 Exercise Class	7	8	9	10
11 Basketball Game	12	13 Exercise Class	14 Internet Class	15	16	17 Movie
18	19	20 Exercise Class	21	22	23	24
25 Basketball Game	26	27 Exercise Class	28 Internet Class	29	30	

When is the _____?
hiking trip
pancake breakfast
writing club meeting

When are the _____?
concerts
cooking classes

Calendar B

September						
S	M	T	W	Th	F	S
				1	2 Concert	3
4	5 Writing Club Meeting	6	7	8 Cooking Class	9	10
11	12	13	14	15	16 Concert	17
18 Hiking Trip	19	20	21	22 Cooking Class	23	24 Pancake Breakfast
25	26	27	28	29	30	

When is the _____?
dance party
movie

When are the _____?
basketball games
exercise classes
Internet classes

Look at the pictures and tell a story.

7
What is she doing now? Draw a picture and finish your story.

January	1
February	2
March	3
April	4
May	5
June	6
July	7
August	8
September	9
October	10
November	11
December	12

drive	drove
give	gave
go	went
lend	lent
lose	lost
sell	sold
send	sent
swim	swam
write	wrote

he – cook – every day.

he – cook – yesterday.

he – cook – right now.

he – cook – tomorrow.

she – drive – every day.

she – drive – yesterday.

she – drive – right now.

she – drive – tomorrow.

they – watch TV– every day.

they – watch TV – yesterday.

they – watch TV – right now.

they – watch TV – tomorrow.

- Put your markers on *Start*.
- Take turns tossing the die (or flipping a coin) to move your marker around the board.
- Follow the instructions in each space.

Where's the school nurse?	She's in the nurse's office.
Where's the librarian?	He's in the library.
Where's the guidance counselor?	He's in the guidance office.
Where are the cafeteria workers?	They're in the cafeteria.
Where's the security officer?	He's in the hall.
Where's the school secretary?	She's in the school office.
Where's the principal?	She's in the principal's office.
Where's the music teacher?	He's in the auditorium.
Where's the P.E. teacher?	She's in the gym.

Floor Plan A

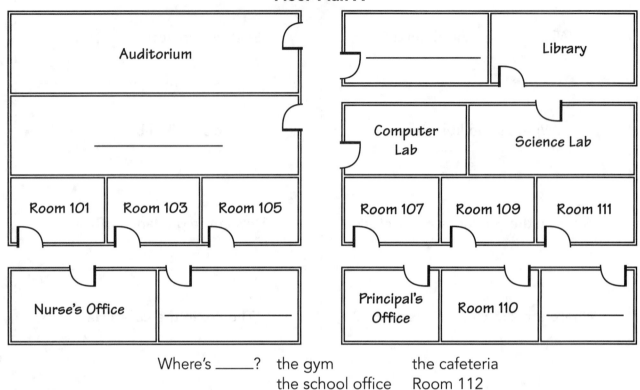

Where's _____? the gym the cafeteria
the school office Room 112

- -

Floor Plan B

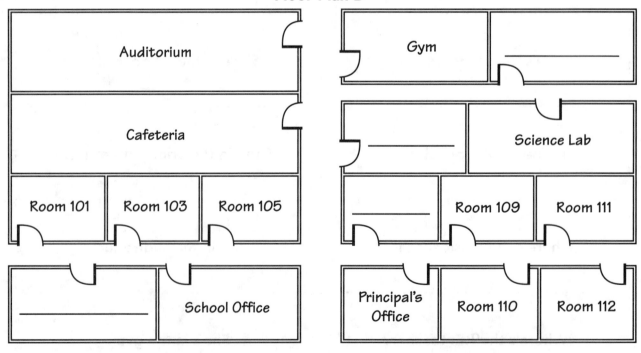

Where's _____? the nurse's office the computer lab
Room 107 the library

Place the CPU and the monitor on a table or desk.

Connect the CPU to the power outlet.

Connect the monitor to the CPU.

Connect the keyboard to the CPU.

Connect the mouse to the CPU.

Connect the CPU to the modem.

Turn on the computer.

To add a printer, connect the printer cable to the CPU.

the power cable – the port – to – connect – .

plug – the surge protector – into – the power cable – .

on – turn – the computer – .

the mouse cable – to – connect – on the keyboard – the port – .

an outlet – plug – the surge protector – into – .

the monitor – turn – on – .

an Ethernet port – to – connect – on the CPU – the cable – .

UNIT 2	**Food Concentration Cards:** *Fruits & Vegetables*	ACTIVITY MASTER **13**

apples	bananas	carrots
grapes	lemons	lettuce
onions	oranges	pears
potatoes	tomatoes	

Where are the cookies?	They're in the cabinet.
Where's the milk?	It's in the refrigerator.
Where's the ice cream?	It's in the freezer.
Where are the bananas?	They're on the counter.
How much milk do you want?	Not too much. Just a little.
How many meatballs do you want?	Not too many. Just a few.
How do you like the chicken?	It's delicious.
How do you like the french fries?	They're delicious.
How much cheese did he buy?	He bought only a little.
How many bananas did she buy?	She bought only a few.

- Put your markers on *Start*.
- Take turns tossing the die (or flipping a coin) to move your marker around the board.
- Follow the instructions in each space.

Where's the ice cream?	It's in the Frozen Food section.
Where are the frozen vegetables?	They're in the Frozen Food section.
Where's the soda?	It's in the Beverages section.
Where's the lettuce?	It's in the Produce section.
Where are the tomatoes?	They're in the Produce section.
Where's the bread?	It's in the Baked Goods section.
Where are the cakes?	They're in the Baked Goods section.
Where's the chicken?	It's in the Meat section.
Where's the cheese?	It's in the Dairy section.
Where are the eggs?	They're in the Dairy section.

Receipt A

Save-Rite Supermarket

2 LB. @ $ _____ LB.	
STRAWBERRIES	7.98
ICE CREAM 1 PT.	4.99
_____ LBS.@ $1.39 LB.	
ONIONS	2.78
4 @ $.49	
ORANGES	1.96
2 LBS. @ $8.99 LB.	
FISH	_____
MILK 1 QT.	1.39
RAISINS	_____
4 @ $.98 GAL	
WATER	_____
8 LBS. @ $.79 LB.	
POTATOES	6.32
TOTAL	$50.81
CASH	$60.00
CHANGE	$_____

How much does a pound of strawberries cost? _____

How many pounds of onions did the person buy? _____

How much did the person pay for fish? _____

How much does a box of raisins cost? _____

How much do two gallons of water cost? _____

How much was the change? _____

Receipt B

Save-Rite Supermarket

2 LB. @ $3.99 LB.	
STRAWBERRIES	7.98
ICE CREAM _____	4.99
2 LBS.@ $1.39 LB.	
ONIONS	2.78
_____ @ $.49	
ORANGES	1.96
2 LBS. @ $8.99 LB.	
FISH	17.98
MILK 1 QT.	_____
RAISINS	3.49
4 @ $.98 GAL	
WATER	3.92
8 LBS. @ _____ LB.	
POTATOES	6.32
TOTAL	$_____
CASH	$60.00
CHANGE	$9.19

How much ice cream did the person buy? _____

How many oranges did the person buy? _____

How much does a quart of milk cost? _____

How much does a pound of potatoes cost? _____

How much did the person pay for the food? _____

Slice a few . . .	carrots.
Slice a little . . .	bread.
Cook the soup . . .	in a saucepan.
Bake the cookies for . . .	15 minutes.
Add a little . . .	salt.
Add a few . . .	grapes.
Pour in a little . . .	honey.
Chop up a little . . .	meat.
Chop up a few . . .	nuts.
Mix in a few . . .	raisins.
Mix in a little . . .	baking soda.

Invitation A

It's a _____ party
for
Robert Mendoza

Please join us!
Time: 7:00 P.M.
Date: _____
Where: The Skyline Restaurant
Address: _____, Bloomington

RSVP by March _____
Telephone: 812-555-0854

What kind of party is it?
What's the date of the party?
What's the address?
When do you need to respond by?

- -

Invitation B

It's a birthday party
for

_____

Please join us!
Time: _____
Date: April 15th
Where: _____
Address: 225 Jefferson Avenue, Bloomington

RSVP by March 30th
Telephone: _____

Who is the party for?
What time is the party?
Where is the party?
What number should you call?

Read the article again. Write Yes or No in each box.

Arriving	Scandinavian Countries and the United States	South America, Italy, and Spain
Arrive at the exact time		
Arrive before the time		
Arrive half an hour after the time		

Food	The Middle East	France, Austria, and Japan
Finish your food		
Always accept food when offered		

Leaving	The United States, Europe, and India	Asia and Central America
Leave soon after eating		

Interview a classmate. Write your partner's responses.

What is polite in your country?

1. Your friends invite you to a 7:00 dinner at their home. What time do you arrive?

   _____

2. How long do you stay at a friend's home after dinner?

   _____

3. How much should you eat at a friend's dinner party? Do you eat more than one serving?

   _____

4. You're still hungry at your friend's dinner. How do you let your host know?

   _____

5. You're full. How do you let your host know?

   _____

6. You're full. Your host offers you more food. What do you do?

   _____

catch a cold	get a sunburn	get seasick
fall	get a shock	drown
get married	grow up	celebrate
put on a helmet	watch your step	put on safety glasses

In five years it will be _____.
(year)

1. Where will you live?

_____

2. What job will you have?

_____

3. Will you speak English well?

_____

4. Will you be married?

_____

5. Will you be happy?

_____

6. Will you be rich or famous?

_____

7. Will you have children?

_____

8. Will you still be friends with _____?

_____

refrigerator	dishwasher	computer
mattress	printer	cell phone
air conditioner	DVD player	

Read the letters again and complete the charts below.

Letter from Marion Kane

	Before	Now
test scores		
class size		
textbooks		
good teachers		

Letter from Ming Lee

	Before	Now
<u>rich neighborhoods</u> buses		
streets		
parks		

	Before	Now
<u>poor neighborhoods</u> buses		
streets		
parks		

Letter from Helen Sanders

	Before	Now
Main Street		
Library		

Schools

Five Years Ago	Now

Public Transportation

Five Years Ago	Now

Parks

Five Years Ago	Now

Streets

Five Years Ago	Now

talented friendly polite talkative	a person
fancy expensive delicious busy	a restaurant
powerful light fast energy-efficient	a laptop computer
exciting short interesting good	a book
healthy cute quiet small	a baby
wide long high expensive fast	a car
reliable clean safe fast efficient	public transportation
hot cold warm rainy snowy	the weather
big modern safe interesting hospitable	a city
delicious spicy warm cold hot	food

May I help you?	Yes. I'd like to return this sweater.
What's the matter with them?	They're too long.
What's the matter with it?	It's too tight.
Would you like to exchange it?	No, thank you. I'd like a refund, please.
Do you have your receipt?	Yes, I do. Here it is.
Where can I find plates and bowls?	In the Housewares department.
Where can I find DVD players?	In the Electronics department.
Where can I find dishwashers?	In the Household Appliances department.
Where can I find suits and ties?	In the Men's Clothing department.
Where can I find skirts and dresses?	In the Women's Clothing department.

Check A

		512

James Lee
Carolyn Lee
982 Pine Avenue
Clinton MI 49236

DATE _____

PAY TO THE
ORDER OF _____ $ | 105.97 |

One hundred five and $^{97}/_{100}$ _____ ⌐ **Dollars**

MID-CITY BANK

For _Internet Bill #220056-91_ _____ _____

⑨⑨⑨⓪⓪⓪①①①: ④④④⑦⑦⑦⑧⑧⑧   ⑤①②

What is the date of the check?
Who is the check to?
Who wrote the check?

- -

Check B

		512

James Lee
Carolyn Lee
982 Pine Avenue
Clinton MI 49236

DATE _3/27/10_____

PAY TO THE
ORDER OF _Cable Cast_____ $ | |

_____ ⌐ **Dollars**

For _____   _James Lee_____

⑨⑨⑨⓪⓪⓪①①①: ④④④⑦⑦⑦⑧⑧⑧   ⑤①②

How much is the check for?
What is the check for?
What is the name of the bank?

1. You bought a sweater 15 days ago. You decided that you don't like the color. You have the receipt. Can you return it?

2. You bought a Christmas tree on December 15th. Can you return it on December 30th?

3. You bought several DVDs last week. They are all opened. Can you return them?

4. You bought a computer 65 days ago. It's defective, but you don't have the receipt. Can you exchange it?

5. You bought a beautiful swimsuit yesterday, but you decided you don't like it. You have the receipt, and the original price tag is still attached. Can you return it?

6. You bought a jacket last month. You paid with a check, and you have the receipt. You want to return it. Can you get a cash refund?

7. You bought a blouse last week. You don't have the receipt. You want to return it because it's ripped. Can you exchange it for another blouse?

8. You bought a coat 29 days ago. It was a Final Sale. You like the coat, but it's too small. You have the receipt, and the original price tag is still attached to the coat. Can you return it?

9. You bought a monitor 46 days ago. You paid cash. Can you return it and get a cash refund?

10. You bought some CDs 30 days ago. They're unopened. You paid with a credit card. Can you return them and get a refund?

11. You bought a watch two weeks ago. You want to return it, and you have the receipt. You paid with a check. Can you get a store credit?

12. You bought a suit last week at Gray's Department Store in Toronto. You're on vacation in London. You want to wear the suit, but you see that the jacket is ripped. You have the receipt, and the original price tag is still attached. Can you return it to the Gray's Department Store in downtown London?

13. _____

14. _____

boring	bright	cheap
comfortable	convenient	dependable
elegant	energetic	fashionable
fast	friendly	funny
generous	helpful	honest
horrible	interesting	kind
large	lazy	lightweight
long	mean	nice
noisy	obnoxious	patient
polite	popular	powerful
pretty	rude	short
sloppy	small	stubborn
talented	ugly	wonderful

balance	deposit	receipt	transfer
cash	exchange	refund	withdrawal
credit card	final sale	store credit	
date of purchase	PIN		

Schedule A

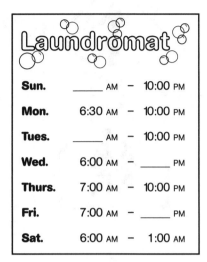

Laundromat		
Sun.	_____ AM –	10:00 PM
Mon.	6:30 AM –	10:00 PM
Tues.	_____ AM –	10:00 PM
Wed.	6:00 AM –	_____ PM
Thurs.	7:00 AM –	10:00 PM
Fri.	7:00 AM –	_____ PM
Sat.	6:00 AM –	1:00 AM

Bakery		
Monday	_____ AM –	6:00 PM
Tuesday	7:30 AM –	7:00 PM
Wednesday	7:30 AM –	8:00 PM
Thursday	7:30 AM –	_____ PM
Friday	7:30 AM –	_____ PM
Saturday	8:00 AM –	7:30 PM
Sunday	_____ AM –	4:00 PM

ICE CREAM SHOP

M	12:00 PM –	10:00 PM
T	_____ AM –	10:00 PM
W	11:00 AM –	_____ PM
Th	_____ AM –	11:00 PM
F	10:00 AM –	12:00 AM
S	10:00 AM –	_____ AM
S	10:00 AM –	6:00 PM

What time does the _____ close on _____?
What time does the _____ open on _____?

Schedule B

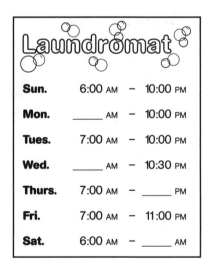

Laundromat		
Sun.	6:00 AM –	10:00 PM
Mon.	_____ AM –	10:00 PM
Tues.	7:00 AM –	10:00 PM
Wed.	_____ AM –	10:30 PM
Thurs.	7:00 AM –	_____ PM
Fri.	7:00 AM –	11:00 PM
Sat.	6:00 AM –	_____ AM

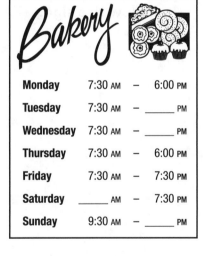

Bakery		
Monday	7:30 AM –	6:00 PM
Tuesday	7:30 AM –	_____ PM
Wednesday	7:30 AM –	_____ PM
Thursday	7:30 AM –	6:00 PM
Friday	7:30 AM –	7:30 PM
Saturday	_____ AM –	7:30 PM
Sunday	9:30 AM –	_____ PM

ICE CREAM SHOP

M	_____ PM –	10:00 PM
T	11:00 AM –	_____ PM
W	11:00 AM –	11:00 PM
Th	11:00 AM –	11:00 PM
F	_____ AM –	12:00 AM
S	10:00 AM –	1:00 AM
S	10:00 AM –	_____ PM

What time does the _____ close on _____?
What time does the _____ open on _____?

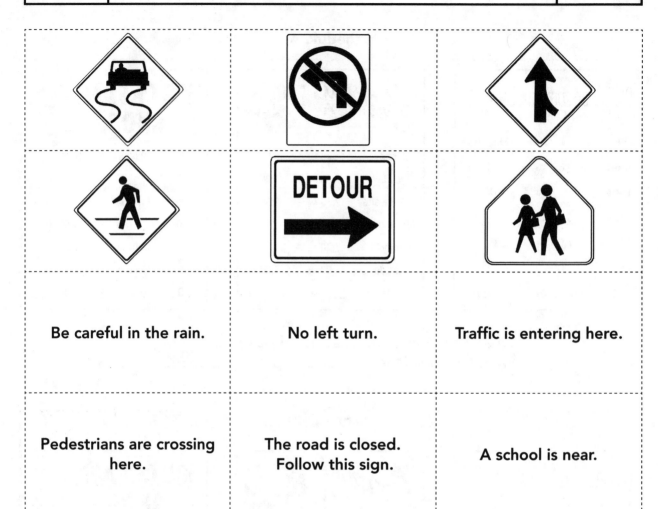

Be careful in the rain.	No left turn.	Traffic is entering here.
Pedestrians are crossing here.	The road is closed. Follow this sign.	A school is near.

Schedule A

Broadway	10:50 AM	11:20 AM	11:41 AM	12:01 PM	12:25 PM
Center Street	_____	11:29 AM	11:50 AM	_____	12:34 PM
Northern Avenue	11:08 AM	_____	11:58 AM	12:18 PM	_____
Lake Boulevard	_____	11:45 AM	_____	12:25 PM	12:49 PM
Park Road	_____	11:56 AM	12:16 PM	_____	1:00 PM

What time does the ___*10:50*___ train get to ___*Center Street*___ ?

- -

Schedule B

Broadway	10:50 AM	11:20 AM	11:41 AM	12:01 PM	12:25 PM
Center Street	10:59 AM	11:29 AM	_____	12:10 PM	_____
Northern Avenue	_____	11:37 AM	11:58 AM	_____	12:42 PM
Lake Boulevard	11:15 AM	_____	12:05 PM	_____	12:49 PM
Park Road	11:26 AM	11:56 AM	_____	12:36 PM	_____

What time does the ___*10:50*___ train get to ___*Northern Avenue*___ ?

**Read the article *Safe Driving* on student text page 70c again.
Check (✓) *Yes* (*safe driving*) or *No* (*not safe driving*) for each statement.**

		Yes	No
1.	Eat while you drive.	____	____
2.	Wear a seat belt.	____	____
3.	Talk on a cell phone while you drive.	____	____
4.	Keep the windshield clean.	____	____
5.	Check your brakes every week.	____	____
6.	Put a child under the age of five in a safety seat.	____	____
7.	Be a slow driver.	____	____
8.	Pay attention to the speed limit.	____	____
9.	Use headlights in rain and fog.	____	____
10.	Take medicine that can make you sleepy before you drive.	____	____
11.	Stay close to the car in front of you.	____	____
12.	Pay attention to other drivers.	____	____
13.	Look before you change lanes.	____	____
14.	Drive fast in the snow.	____	____
15.	Have your license, car registration, and insurance card with you when you drive.	____	____

Wear . . .	a seat belt.
Take care . . .	of your car.
Check . . .	your brakes.
Pay attention . . .	to traffic signs.
Slow . . .	down in rain, snow, and fog.
Don't talk on . . .	your cell phone.
Small children should ride . . .	in child safety seats.
Be . . .	careful.
Don't take . . .	medicine that makes you sleepy.
Use your headlights in . . .	rain, snow, and fog.

airport	bakery	bank
barber shop	baseball stadium	book store
bus station	cafeteria	church
clinic	concert hall	courthouse
department store	drug store	fire station
flower shop	gas station	hardware store
high school	hospital	hotel
ice cream shop	laundromat	library
motel	museum	park
parking garage	parking lot	pet shop
playground	police station	post office
restaurant	shoe store	shopping mall
supermarket	toy store	train station
university	zoo	

Ask: "How do you get to school?"
Write the person's name in the second column.
Add up the number of people.

How?	Names	How Many?
walk		
take the bus		
take the subway		
take the train		
ride a bicycle		
drive		

What are your job skills?
Where do you work now?
Where did you work before your current job?

Job Skills and Work History

Find someone who . . .

1. can speak Spanish. _____

2. can drive a truck. _____

3. can fix cars. _____

4. can install light fixtures. _____

5. can cook very well. _____

6. works in a restaurant. _____

7. works in a hospital. _____

8. works in a bank. _____

9. worked in a store. _____

10. worked in an office. _____

PT	hr.	FT	yrs.
exp.	req.	excel.	M–F
pref.	wk.	mo.	eves.
2+	part-time	hour	full-time
years	experience	required	excellent
Monday to Friday	preferred	week	month
evenings	more than two		

Chef. PT. $30+/hr.	Chef. Part-time. More than $30 an hour.
Chef. FT. $30/hr.	Chef. Full-time. $30 an hour.
FT Custodian needed. Days. M-F. No exp. req.	Full-time custodian needed. Days. Monday to Friday. No experience required.
FT Custodian needed. Eves. M-F. No exp. req.	Full-time custodian needed. Evenings. Monday to Friday. No experience required.
PT Driver. Eves. only. 1 yr. exp. req.	Part-time driver. Evenings only. One year experience required.
PT Driver. Eves. only. 1+ yr. exp. pref.	Part-time driver. Evenings only. More than one year experience preferred.
FT Secretary. M-F. Excel. salary & benefits. Call Pat at (201) 555-2323.	Full-time secretary. Monday to Friday. Excellent salary and benefits. Call Pat at (201) 555-2323.
FT Secretary. M-F. $2100-2200/mo. Call Pat at (201) 555-2323.	Full-time secretary. Monday to Friday. Salary between $2100 and $2200 a month. Call Pat at (201) 555-2323.
Toy World. FT Cashier. Exp. req. $9+/hr. Call Bob (201) 555-8866.	Toy World. Full-time cashier. Experience required. More than $9 an hour. Call Bob at (201) 555-8866.
Toy World. PT Cashier. Eves. req. $235/wk. Call Bob (201) 555-8866.	Toy World. Part-time cashier. Evenings required. $235 a week. Call Bob at (201) 555-8866.

Pay Stub Bingo

deductions	gross pay	overtime rate
earnings	Medicare	regular rate
federal tax	net pay	state tax
FICA		

Pay Stub A

Linda Chen		Pay Period 10/5–10/11	
Earnings	**Rate**	**Hours**	**Total**
Regular		35	490.00
Overtime			
Gross Pay			
Taxes & Deductions			
Federal Tax			
State Tax			14.00
FICA/Medicare			
Health			24.00
Total			135.00
Net Pay			535.00

How much is Linda's regular rate of pay?

How much federal tax did she pay?

How much was her FICA/Medicare deduction?

How much did she earn before taxes and deductions?

Pay Stub B

Linda Chen		Pay Period 10/5–10/11	
Earnings	**Rate**	**Hours**	**Total**
Regular	14.00		490.00
Overtime			180.00
Gross Pay			670.00
Taxes & Deductions			
Federal Tax			61.00
State Tax			
FICA/Medicare			36.00
Health			
Total			135.00
Net Pay			

How many regular hours did Linda work this pay period?

How much state tax did she pay?

How much was her health insurance deduction?

How much did she earn after taxes and deductions?

Read the accident report on student text page 80e again. Find words in the accident report that have the same meaning as the underlined words below.

1. Please complete this report and <u>give it</u> to the Personnel Department.

   _____

2. Name of injured <u>worker</u>.

   _____

3. Where did the accident <u>happen</u>?

   _____

4. How did the employee get <u>hurt</u>?

   _____

5. <u>What is</u> the injury and the part(s) of the body injured?

   _____

6. <u>Doctor's</u> name.

   _____

7. What <u>caused</u> the accident?

   _____

awkwardly	dishonestly	neatly
badly	early	slowly
carefully	impolitely	softly

Ask students: "Are you prepared for an emergency at home?"

	Yes	No
Do you have a list of emergency phone numbers near the telephone?	_____	_____
Do you have a first-aid kit in a convenient place?	_____	_____
Do you change the batteries in your smoke detector twice a year?	_____	_____
Do you keep a fire extinguisher in your kitchen?	_____	_____
Do you know how to turn off your utilities?	_____	_____
Do you know when to dial 911?	_____	_____

CPR	ointment	swallow
dressing	pulse	victim
Heimlich maneuver	sterile	wound

Duck.	Put your face into your arm.	Cover your head and neck with your arms.
Hold on to the doorway.	Drop to your knees.	Turn away from windows.
Hold on to a table.	Fill your car with gas.	Fill bottles with water.
Cover windows with tape.	Watch TV.	Bring trash cans and bicycles from your yard into your home.
Get down under a desk.	Cover your head with a book.	Get into a doorway.
Cover your head with a desk.	Cover your head with one hand.	Put batteries into flashlights.

trip over something	bite	break into an apartment
burn yourself	crash into someone	cut yourself
hold on to a table	deliver something	drop to your knees
faint	fall	get off a bus
get on a train	get out of a car	lose something
open a window	poke yourself in the eye	spill a glass of water
take a test	take a walk	get a flat tire

dropped – she – walking – of – the – her – while – she – packages – store. – was – out

he – bridge. – a – flat – while – he – over – was – got – driving – the – tire

I – while – studying – was – the – bike – library. – at – someone – stole – my

he – was – cut – he – himself – slicing – carrots. – while

I – was – while – I – bus. – getting – the – tripped – off

I – glasses. – myself – on – in – the – eye – was – poked – while – I – putting – my

him – saw – he – while – was – train. – getting – we – on – the

delivering – a – bit – her – while – dog – she – was – mail. – the

she – waiting – while - taxi. – she – was – fainted – for – a

saw – walking – they – accident – they – the – while – school. – were – to

I burned my hand while I was cooking!	Put it in cold water.
I got a household product in my eyes!	Rinse it with water for 15 minutes.
I just got stung by a bee!	Put some ice on it.
I just got a shock!	I'll turn off the power.
He isn't breathing!	Give him CPR.
She's choking!	Do the Heimlich maneuver.
My cut is bleeding badly!	Put pressure on it for 10 minutes.
A dog bit my leg!	Wash it with soap and water.
A hurricane is coming!	We need to evacuate now.
I think it's an earthquake!	Quick! Get under the table!

- Put your markers on *Start*.
- Take turns tossing the die (or flipping a coin) to move your marker around the board.
- Follow the instructions in each space.

Finish the sentence!

A can of paint fell on him while . . .

In 30 seconds . . .

name three things you should do if there is a hurricane watch.

? **?**

Answer the question:

What is a first-aid treatment for a burn?

? **?**

Answer the question:

What is a first-aid treatment for bleeding?

In 30 seconds . . .

name three things you should do in an earthquake.

What were you doing yesterday morning at 8:00 A.M.?

Draw your answer.

Everyone has to guess what you were doing.

Finish the sentence!

They tripped and fell while . . .

? **?**

Answer the question:

What is a first-aid treatment for a bee sting?

What were you doing yesterday afternoon at 4:00 P.M.?

Draw your answer.

Everyone has to guess what you were doing.

In 30 seconds . . .

name four situations when you should call 911.

Ask everyone in your group what they were doing yesterday evening at 8:00 P.M. Then repeat what they said.

? **?**

Answer the question:

What is a first-aid treatment for an electric shock?

Do you have any one-bedroom apartments for rent?	Yes. We have a one-bedroom apartment downtown.
How much is the rent?	It's $1,000 a month.
Does that include utilities?	No, it doesn't.
Would you like to see the apartment?	Yes, please.
Is there a security deposit?	Yes there is. We require one month's rent as a deposit.
Is parking included?	No, it isn't. You have to pay extra for parking.
Are pets allowed in the building?	Yes, they are.
Is there public transportation nearby?	Yes. There's a bus stop in front of the building.

Rental Form A

City-Side Realty

2–Bedroom Apartment	151 Winter Street
Rent:	
Security Deposit:	First and last months' rent
Utilities:	
Parking:	Included
Pets:	
Public transportation:	Bus stop two blocks away

How much is the rent?
Does the rent include utilities?
Are pets allowed?

- -

Rental Form B

City-Side Realty

2–Bedroom Apartment	151 Winter Street
Rent:	$1,350
Security Deposit:	
Utilities:	Not Included
Parking:	
Pets:	Okay
Public transportation:	

Is there a security deposit?
Is parking included?
Is there public transportation nearby?

air conditioning	a/c	dishwasher	d/w
apartment	apt.	elevator	elev.
balcony	balc.	kitchen	kit.
basement	bsmt.	living room	liv. rm.
bedroom	BR	manager	mgr.
building	bldg.	parking	pkg.
dining room	din. rm.	refrigerator	refrig.
superintendent	supt.	bathroom	BA

beautiful	beaut.	month	mo.
available	avail.	near	nr.
excellent	excel.	schools	schls.
floor	flr.	two-family house	2-fam. hse.
immediately	immed.	utilities	util.
included	incl.	with	w/
large	lg.		

Lg., sunny, 1 BR apt. w/ balc. Avail. immed. Call bldg. mgr.	A large sunny one-bedroom apartment with a balcony. Available immediately. Call the building manager.
Lg. beaut. 2 BR, 1 BA apt. w/ balc. Lge. kit. w/ new appliances. Call supt.	A large beautiful two-bedroom, one-bathroom apartment with a balcony. It has a large kitchen with new appliances. Call the superintendent.
Apt. on 2nd flr. Elev. in bldg., laundry rm. in bsmt.	An apartment on the second floor. There's an elevator in the building and a laundry room in the basement.
Apt. on 7th flr., mod. bldg. Laundry rm. in bsmt., pkg. garage.	An apartment on the seventh floor of a modern building. There's a laundry room in the basement and a parking garage.
3 BR apt. in 2-fam. hse. $2300/mo. Util. not incl.	A three-bedroom apartment in a two-family house. The rent is $2300 a month. Utilities are not included.
1 BR apt. in 3-fam. hse. $1100/mo. Util. incl.	A one-bedroom apartment in a three-family house. The rent is $1100 a month. Utilities are included.
2 BR apt.,1.5 BA, din. rm., liv. rm., lg. eat-in-kit. w/ new refrig. & d/w.	A two-bedroom apartment with one and a half bathrooms, a dining room, living room, and large eat-in-kitchen with a new refrigerator and dishwasher.
3 BR apt., 2 BA, a/c. Nr. excel. schls. $1900/mo. Avail. immed.	A three-bedroom apartment with two bathrooms and air conditioning. Near excellent schools. The rent is $1900 a month. It's available immediately.

clumsy	large	sick
dark	light	weak
difficult	long	young
full	noisy	

Role Play 1—Student A

You're a secretary in Doctor Wong's office. Someone is calling the office. You have only two appointments available—this afternoon at 4:45 and tomorrow morning at 10:00.

Role Play 1—Student B

You have a stiff neck and a headache. You want to make an appointment with Doctor Wong. You need an appointment as soon as possible.

Role Play 2—Student A

You're a waiter. You have a very bad backache. You're calling in sick. Your doctor said you must rest your back for a few more days.

Role Play 2—Student B

You're the supervisor at a restaurant. A waiter is calling in sick. This employee calls in sick very often. You're frustrated with this employee.

Role Play 3—Student A

You're a parent. Your daughter has a fever and a sore throat. She can't go to school today. You're calling her school. Your daughter's name is Wendy Lopez. Her teacher is Ms. Kline.

Role Play 3—Student B

You're the secretary in a school office. When parents call to report absences, they need to tell you the child's name, the child's teacher, and the reason for the absence.

antacid	expiration date	pharmacy
antihistamine	over-the-counter medicine	prescription medicine
decongestant	pain reliever	side effects

How do you get prescription medicine?	How do you get over-the-counter medicine?
Who can write a prescription?	Who can fill a prescription and explain the medicine to the patient?
What is an expiration date?	What medicine can you take for a stuffy nose?
What medicine can you take for a headache?	What medicine can you take for allergies?
What are the side effects of some pain medicines?	What does the warning label tell you?
When should you throw away medicine?	Why is it dangerous to take two or more medicines at the same time?
What does dosage mean?	Why should you read a medicine label carefully?
What are three different kinds of ailments?	What should you do if you are taking over-the-counter medicine and you don't feel better?

measure the patient's height	measure the patient's weight	do some blood tests
take the patient's blood pressure	take a chest X-ray	lead the patient into a room
shake hands with the patient	examine the patient's throat	examine the patient's eyes
listen to the patient's heart with a stethoscope	examine the patient's ears	take the patient's pulse

apples	brown rice	butter
cake	candy	cheese
cookies	eggs	fatty meat
fish	french fries	grapefruit
ice cream	lean meat	margarine
mayonnaise	nuts	onions
peppers	potato chips	potatoes
raisins	rice	salt
skim milk	sugar	tomatoes
whole wheat bread	yogurt	

I have a stuffy nose. What should I do?	You should take some decongestant.
I have a sore throat. What should I do?	You should use some throat lozenges.
I have a stomachache. What should I do?	You should take some antacid.
I have a backache. Do you have any advice?	You should take some pain reliever.
I'm a little too heavy. Do you have advice?	You should stop eating rich desserts.
My knees hurt. Do you have any advice?	You should stop jogging every day.
I have high blood pressure. Do you have any suggestions?	You should eat less salt.
I have allergies. What should I do?	You should take some antihistamines.
I have a cough. I'm taking cough syrup, but it isn't helping. What should I do?	You should see a doctor about your cough.

Brown rice is a whole grain.	Skim milk is a low-fat food.
A lab technician does blood tests.	An X-ray technician listens to your heart.
A scale measures your weight.	A cardiogram measures your height.
People shouldn't drink water. They should drink soda instead.	A checkup is a physical examination by a doctor.
Calcium is a mineral.	Salt is bad for people with high blood pressure.
Sugar doesn't have any nutrients.	It's better to fry food than to grill, broil, or microwave it.
You shouldn't take medicine before its expiration date.	You have to talk to a doctor to get an over-the-counter medicine.
The dosage tells you how much medicine to take and how often to take it.	Prescription medicine has more possible side effects than over-the-counter medicine.
You should try to eat food that is high in fat and low in vitamins.	You should tell your doctor about all the medicines you're taking.

A

message 1

Peggy —

_____ called

_____ - _____ - _____

message 2

Mark —

Sam called

921-334-6501

message 3

Bill —

_____ called

_____ - _____ - _____

message 4

Anna —

Dr. Sanchez called

413-489-5623

- -

B

message 1

Peggy —

Marta called

718-552-8390

message 2

Mark —

_____ called

_____ - _____ - _____

message 3

Bill —

Ms. Miller called

912-834-1906

message 4

Anna —

_____ called

_____ - _____ - _____

Someone is breaking into my apartment!	Call 911.
The elevator doesn't work in our building, and our landlord won't repair it.	Call the Building Inspector.
A tree fell down in the road!	Call the Highway Department.
Is there a concert in Roger Park today?	I don't know. Call the Parks and Recreation Department.
How old does a child have to be to go to kindergarten?	I'm not sure. Call the School Department.
We just found a lost puppy in the street!	Call the Animal Control Office.
What time is the children's story hour?	I don't know. Call the library.
What can we do with all these old bottles?	I don't know. Call the Recycling Department.
I think that restaurant is really dirty. I don't think the food is safe to eat.	You should call the Board of Health.

LAST NAME, First name	Address	Telephone Number

Our Class Directory

BOOKS	Asian Book Store
Betty's Best Books	Bins & Nibbles
Canterbury Book Shop	Richmond Square Books
Willow State University Book Store	Winston Book Shop
World Travel Book Store	BOOTS
AMK Boots	Burt's Boots
Milton's Shoes and Boots for Men	Weather-All Boots
Work World Boots and Footwear	BOXES
Container Corporation	Cutter's Box Supply
Springfield Box Company	Storage Plus

Ask: "What kind of phone do you use?"
Write the person's name in the second column.
Add up the number of people.

Kind of Phone	Names	How Many?
Cell Phone		
Landline Phone at Home		
Both: Cell Phone and Landline Phone at Home		

Calling Directory Information

Advantages (+)	Disadvantages (–)

Using Telephone Directories

Advantages (+)	Disadvantages (–)

Interview a classmate. Write your partner's responses.

What do you do before you call a repairperson? Do you have any household solutions to these common problems?

1. Your toilet doesn't flush properly.

_____

2. Your kitchen sink is clogged.

_____

3. Your key is stuck in the lock.

_____

4. Your window is stuck and won't open easily.

_____

5. The burners on your stove don't light.

_____

6. Your dishwasher doesn't turn on.

_____

7. Your kitchen faucet is dripping.

_____

8. The water in your toilet tank keeps running.

_____

Carol's kitchen sink was clogged.

She called the building manager and told him about the problem.

The building manager didn't come to fix it.

So Carol called the building manager *again* about the problem.

The building manager *still* didn't come.

Then Carol called a plumber.

The plumber came to fix the drain.

Carol paid the plumber with her own money.

Carol deducted the cost of the repairs from her rent the next month.

Carol is happy she did that. She knows her rights as a tenant!

- Put your markers on *Start*.
- Take turns tossing the die (or flipping a coin) to move your marker around the board.
- Follow the instructions in each space.

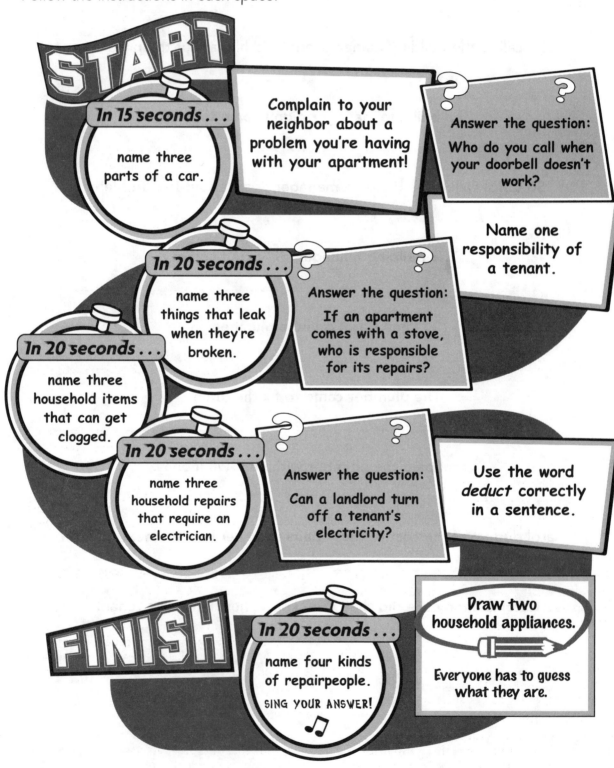

START

In 15 seconds . . . name three parts of a car.

Complain to your neighbor about a problem you're having with your apartment!

Answer the question: Who do you call when your doorbell doesn't work?

Name one responsibility of a tenant.

In 20 seconds . . . name three things that leak when they're broken.

Answer the question: If an apartment comes with a stove, who is responsible for its repairs?

In 20 seconds . . . name three household items that can get clogged.

In 20 seconds . . . name three household repairs that require an electrician.

Answer the question: Can a landlord turn off a tenant's electricity?

Use the word *deduct* correctly in a sentence.

FINISH

In 20 seconds . . . name four kinds of repairpeople. SING YOUR ANSWER!

Draw two household appliances. Everyone has to guess what they are.

Side by Side Plus 2
Unit Achievement Tests & Assessment Resources
Teacher Notes

The *Side by Side Plus 2* Multilevel Activity and Achievement Test Book and CD-ROM offers the following reproducible resources for student assessment and record-keeping:

- Thirteen reproducible Unit Achievement Tests—one for each unit

- A Listening Script for the listening activities in the unit achievement tests

- An Answer Sheet for use with all tests

- An Answer Key

- Learner Assessment Records for evaluating and documenting each student's test performance and progress, including easy-to-use scoring rubrics for assessing writing and speaking skills

- A Learner Progress Chart for students to use to record their test scores and to chart their progress

GOAL OF THE UNIT ACHIEVEMENT TESTS

The unit achievement tests are designed to assess student progress and prepare students for the types of standardized tests and performance assessments used by many instructional programs. Such tests have become common tools for assessing students' educational advancement and for evaluating programs' effectiveness in meeting outcome-based performance standards.

TEST CONTENT

The tests include multiple-choice questions that assess vocabulary, grammar, reading, listening skills, life-skill competencies, and document literacy tasks (such as reading medicine labels, signs, and everyday documents); short-answer questions that cover learning skills such as chronological order and word categorization; writing tasks including filling out forms, a check, and a schedule; narrative writing assessments that can be evaluated with a standardized scoring rubric and be collected in portfolios of students' work; and speaking performance assessments designed to stimulate face-to-face interactions between students, for evaluation by the teacher using a standardized scoring rubric, or for self-evaluation by students.

Students can record their answers to each test's multiple-choice questions in two ways. They can "bubble in" their answers directly on the test page, or they can use the Answer Sheet for useful and realistic practice placing answers on a separate sheet rather than in a test booklet. Students can answer the other questions by writing directly on the test page. The open-ended writing assessments should be completed on a separate sheet.

USING THE TESTS

You can use the tests in a variety of ways to carefully develop students' test-taking skills. For the first few tests, it will be helpful to do each section of the test separately. Go over each section as a class, and then have students try to answer the questions in that section. Make sure students understand the question format and any example that is provided. For the next few tests, preview all the sections at once, make sure students understand all the formats, and then have them take the test in its entirety. For the remaining tests, in order to simulate a real test-taking situation, have students answer all the questions without any preview of the material.

Over time, you can modify other aspects of the test-taking experience to develop students' skills. For example, for the first few tests, you might allow students to ask for help when they have difficulty understanding a question format. Later, it will be better not to allow students to ask for help during a test. Also, you may want to have students do some or most of the tests on an untimed basis, allowing them as much time as they need to answer all the questions. Eventually, though, it is good practice for students to take some of the tests on a timed basis, especially if they will experience timed tests in your program. (If you use timed tests, let students complete the unfinished items later in class or at home so they benefit from the practice.)

STRATEGIES FOR USING THE TEST FORMATS

We encourage you to use the unit achievement tests in the way that is most appropriate given the needs and abilities of your students as well as your teaching style, classroom situation, and the assessment requirements of your program. Here are some strategies for using the different test formats:

MULTIPLE-CHOICE QUESTIONS

Each test includes 40 multiple-choice questions. Have students indicate their answers by bubbling in the correct letter in the answer grid at the bottom of the test page or on the separate reproducible answer sheet. In this way, students practice the coordination skills involved in matching questions in a test booklet with their corresponding answer lines on a separate answer sheet.

The different sets of multiple-choice questions in each test cover a range of topics and language skills:

LIFESKILL COMPETENCY questions focus on relevant topics and vocabulary.

GRAMMAR IN CONTEXT sections help students practice functional language and grammar through contextualized conversations. (After the test, students will benefit from practicing these conversations in pairs or as a class.)

READING COMPREHENSION sections include traditional reading passages and authentic lifeskill reading material such as calendars, schedules, ads, receipts, signs, medicine labels, telephone directory listings, a menu, and a floor plan.

CLOZE READING sections in some tests develop students' ability to use their knowledge of vocabulary and grammar to select the correct words to complete a narrative passage.

LISTENING ASSESSMENT sections evaluate listening comprehension skills. The Listening Script contains the exercise instructions, the questions, and the listening passage. Have students read along silently as you read the exercise instructions and the questions one or more times. In this way, students know what information to listen for when they hear the listening passage. Then read the listening passage one or more times and have students answer the questions.

SHORT ANSWER QUESTIONS

Workbook-style activities in some tests have students practice basic literacy tasks and learning skills as they fill in blanks, categorize words, or put events into chronological order. Make sure students write their answers legibly in the spaces provided.

WRITING ASSESSMENTS

Writing tasks include forms to fill out, short questions to answer, and paragraphs to write about familiar topics covered in the corresponding unit of *Side by Side Plus*. Have students write their answers on the test page if space is provided. Otherwise, they should write their answers on a separate sheet of paper. These writing assessments can be evaluated using the scoring

rubrics provided on the Learner Assessment Record sheets and can be collected in portfolios of students' work.

SPEAKING ASSESSMENTS

The speaking assessment section at the end of each test provides a checklist of questions designed to stimulate brief, face-to-face conversations between students. First, preview the questions to make sure students understand the vocabulary. Then have students practice the questions in one or more of the following ways:

PAIR PRACTICE: Have students work in pairs, taking turns asking and answering the questions.

LINE CONVERSATIONS: Have students stand in two lines facing each other. Each pair of facing students should take turns asking and answering a question (or two or more questions if you prefer). After sufficient time for this practice, say "Move," and have one line of students move down one position while the other line remains in place. (The student at the end of the line moves to the beginning of the line.) In this way, new pairs are created and students can practice with another partner. Continue the line conversations until students have practiced asking and answering all the questions.

"ROUND ROBIN": Have students circulate around the room and ask each other the questions. Students should move on to another person after they have taken turns asking and answering a question.

To evaluate students, you can observe them as they practice asking and answering the questions during the above activities. Or, have pairs of students present some of the questions and answers to the entire class or just for you. Score each student separately using the scoring rubrics provided on the Learner Assessment Record sheets.

(CLASSROOM MANAGEMENT TIP: To save time, you might begin the test-taking practice by previewing the Speaking Assessment questions and having students practice them using one or more of the suggestions above. Then have students take the written test in class. While they are occupied, call out students in pairs to present to you some of the Speaking Assessment questions and answers, perhaps in the hallway or in an adjacent room, so the rest of the class is not disturbed.)

USING THE LEARNER ASSESSMENT RECORDS

A reproducible Learner Assessment Record for each unit achievement test is designed for easy scoring of a student's performance. It provides specific scoring rubrics for all multiple-choice questions, short-answer questions, writing assessments, and speaking assessments. Each test is scored on a 100-point scale, providing a consistent means to evaluate student achievement of topics, vocabulary, grammar, and listening, speaking, reading, and writing skills. The Learner Assessment Records can serve as documentation of students' progress during the course of the instructional program.

TEST-TAKING STRATEGIES FOR STUDENTS

As students work with the tests, focus on strategies that students need to develop in order to perform well on authentic tests. Work on these strategies at a pace and intensity that are appropriate for the needs and abilities of your students.

BUBBLING IN THE BUBBLES

Make sure students know how to use a pencil to fill in a bubble completely on an answer grid so that the answer is recorded. Explain if necessary how the answer sheet on a standardized test is scored by a machine. (You may want to have a supply of Number 2 pencils available for test-taking practice.)

ERASURES AND STRAY MARKS

Students should be sure to erase completely any bubbled-in answer that they wish to change. They should also be sure to erase any stray marks they may have accidentally made on a page.

BUBBLING IN ON THE CORRECT LINE OF THE ANSWER SHEET

Make sure students avoid some common mistakes when recording their answers on the answer sheet. They shouldn't put the answer to a sample question as the first answer on the answer sheet. If they skip a question, they need to be sure to skip the corresponding line on the answer sheet as well. (Encourage students to make a mark on the test page next to any question they have skipped so they can locate these questions quickly when they come back to them.)

FOLLOWING DIRECTIONS

Students should always look at the instructions and any example carefully so that they know what to do with each set of questions. (For example, a common mistake is for students to fill out a form that might appear on a test page rather than to follow the instructions to answer questions *about* the form.)

MULTIPLE-CHOICE STRATEGIES

When students don't know the answer to a multiple-choice question, they should learn to eliminate the choice or choices that they know are incorrect. By doing this, they might arrive at the correct answer, or they may narrow down the number of possible answers and then guess. (If you wish, have students actually cross out on the test page the letters of answer choices they can eliminate so that they can focus on a narrower set of choices.)

MULTIPLE-CHOICE "TRAPS"

After students have taken a test, go over the multiple-choice questions and point out the *distractors* (the wrong choices). Have students notice the distractors that are "traps"—choices that are tricky for one or more reasons. For example, a choice might have correct information but incorrect grammar, or correct grammar but incorrect information, or information that is somewhat related to the question but doesn't answer it.

ANSWERING EASY QUESTIONS FIRST

Students should understand that tests are often arranged so that within each set of questions, easier items come before more difficult ones. Especially when students begin practicing the tests on a timed basis, they should be careful not to spend too much time dwelling on difficult questions. Encourage them to keep moving by answering the easier questions first and then going back to the more difficult ones. Make sure that if they skip a question, they also skip the corresponding line on the answer sheet. (Suggest that students make a mark on the test page next to any question they have skipped so they can quickly locate these questions later.)

PACING

Prepare students to take tests on a timed basis. Have them look briefly at a test before taking it in order to identify the number and types of questions in each section and to decide approximately how much time they should plan to spend on each section. Then have them take the test and keep track of their pacing and progress. If they are falling behind, they should not dwell on the most difficult questions, but instead move on to other test sections and then go back later to the difficult items. Make sure students allow enough time after their first pass through a test to go back to unanswered questions and then to check their work.

ANSWERING SHORT-ANSWER QUESTIONS APPROPRIATELY

Students should be sure they understand what is expected in a short answer—for example, a word, a phrase, or a complete sentence; a complete word or an abbreviation; a dollar amount or measurement written with words or with symbols.

Students often write more or less than expected in a short answer, and they frequently use incorrect symbols or notation in answers that would otherwise be correct.

WRITING PARAGRAPHS

Point out to students the features of their writing that will be evaluated: appropriateness of content, spelling, punctuation and capitalization, grammar, and completeness of sentences. Encourage students to write paragraphs that are as complete and correct as possible, even if they are not sure they have understood the question or topic exactly right, since their writing will be evaluated based on these different dimensions. Identify common problems and weaknesses you observe in students' writing assessments and devote some class time to workshops on these areas.

CHECKING ANSWERS

Make sure students allow enough time to go over their work before handing in a test. They should first try to answer any questions they have skipped and then go over their work to check it. Caution students that they shouldn't change an answer unless they know it is incorrect. If they have guessed an answer and they are still not sure of the correct choice, their first guess is more likely to be the accurate one.

OTHER FORMS OF ASSESSMENT

In addition to using the unit achievement tests, you should plan to use a variety of other forms of assessment with your students. Alternative assessment activities that involve students performing classroom or real-life tasks, playing games, or participating in role plays, simulations, and other performance-based activities should be part of a well-rounded assessment program. Using portfolio assessment strategies to keep files of student work (for example, homework, in-class writing, creative projects, teacher evaluations, and student self-evaluations) creates a much more comprehensive picture of student achievement and progress than that represented by a set of test scores.

LEARNER PROGRESS CHART

The reproducible Learner Progress Chart enables students to record their test scores and chart their progress. You may want to keep the charts in a folder and have students update them as each test is completed.

INTEGRATING SCANS SKILLS

For programs that integrate the objectives of the Secretary's Commission on Achieving Necessary Skills (SCANS), it is very appropriate to give students responsibility for the day-to-day management of classroom logistics, such as recording attendance, obtaining supplies and equipment, or making copies of lesson handouts. Students can also take responsibility for aspects of their assessment, including scoring the Unit Achievement Tests, copying blank answer sheets, graphing their performance on their Learner Progress Chart, and maintaining their student portfolios.

A ASKING PERSONAL INFORMATION QUESTIONS

Choose the sentence with the same meaning.

Example:

What's your age?

- Ⓐ How tall are you?
- Ⓑ What's your weight?
- Ⓒ How old are you?
- Ⓓ Where were you born?   Ⓐ Ⓑ ● Ⓓ

1. What's your date of birth?

- Ⓐ What country are you from?
- Ⓑ Where were you born?
- Ⓒ What's your marital status?
- Ⓓ When were you born?

2. What's your marital status?

- Ⓐ How much do you weigh?
- Ⓑ Are you married or single?
- Ⓒ What country are you from?
- Ⓓ How tall are you?

3. Where were you born?

- Ⓐ What's your height?
- Ⓑ What's your weight?
- Ⓒ What's your date of birth?
- Ⓓ What's your place of birth?

4. How tall are you?

- Ⓐ What's your height?
- Ⓑ What's your weight?
- Ⓒ What's your age?
- Ⓓ What's your nationality?

5. What country are you from?

- Ⓐ What's your marital status?
- Ⓑ When were you born?
- Ⓒ What's your nationality?
- Ⓓ Are you married or single?

B ANSWERING PERSONAL INFORMATION QUESTIONS

Choose the correct answer.

Example:

What's your zip code?

- Ⓐ 415.
- Ⓑ 10027.
- Ⓒ 027-48-9451.
- Ⓓ #12-G.   Ⓐ ● Ⓒ Ⓓ

6. What's your telephone number?

- Ⓐ 283-73-2851.
- Ⓑ (215) 627-9382.
- Ⓒ 97623.
- Ⓓ 1267-B.

7. What's your height?

- Ⓐ 155 pounds.
- Ⓑ 27 years old.
- Ⓒ Five feet eight inches.
- Ⓓ Brown.

8. What's your nationality?

- Ⓐ Mexican.
- Ⓑ Los Angeles.
- Ⓒ California.
- Ⓓ Mexico City.

9. What's your weight?

- Ⓐ 22214.
- Ⓑ Five feet three inches.
- Ⓒ Married.
- Ⓓ 168 pounds.

10. What's your social security number?

- Ⓐ 124.
- Ⓑ 227-53-8716.
- Ⓒ (617) 372-9106.
- Ⓓ 33928.

....

1 Ⓐ Ⓑ Ⓒ Ⓓ   4 Ⓐ Ⓑ Ⓒ Ⓓ   7 Ⓐ Ⓑ Ⓒ Ⓓ   10 Ⓐ Ⓑ Ⓒ Ⓓ

2 Ⓐ Ⓑ Ⓒ Ⓓ   5 Ⓐ Ⓑ Ⓒ Ⓓ   8 Ⓐ Ⓑ Ⓒ Ⓓ

3 Ⓐ Ⓑ Ⓒ Ⓓ   6 Ⓐ Ⓑ Ⓒ Ⓓ   9 Ⓐ Ⓑ Ⓒ Ⓓ

Go to the next page ▷

C   PERSONAL INFORMATION FORM

Name: (1)

Street: (2)   Apartment: (3)

City: (4)   State: (5)   Zip Code: (6)

Social Security Number: (7)   Country of Origin: (8)

Telephone: (9)   E-Mail: (10)   Age: (11)

Height: (12)   Weight: (13)   Eye Color: (14)   Hair Color: (15)

Look at the information. Choose the correct line on the form.

Example:

#201-C
- (A) Line 1
- (B) Line 2
- (C) Line 3
- (D) Line 4

(A) (B) ● (D)

13. andre27@ail.com
- (A) Line 1
- (B) Line 6
- (C) Line 7
- (D) Line 10

11. 5479 Washington Boulevard
- (A) Line 2
- (B) Line 4
- (C) Line 8
- (D) Line 10

14. 5 ft. 10 in.
- (A) Line 3
- (B) Line 12
- (C) Line 13
- (D) Line 14

12. China
- (A) Line 1
- (B) Line 2
- (C) Line 8
- (D) Line 10

15. blue
- (A) Line 12
- (B) Line 13
- (C) Line 14
- (D) Line 15

- -

11 (A) (B) (C) (D)   13 (A) (B) (C) (D)   15 (A) (B) (C) (D)

12 (A) (B) (C) (D)   14 (A) (B) (C) (D)

Go to the next page

Choose the correct answer to complete the conversation.

Example:

What's your _____?
- Ⓐ city
- Ⓑ nationality
- Ⓒ height
- ● name

16. My name _____ Marie Isabel Fuentes.
- Ⓐ am
- Ⓑ is
- Ⓒ are
- Ⓓ call

17. _____ do you spell your last name?
- Ⓐ How
- Ⓑ Who
- Ⓒ Where
- Ⓓ Why

18. _____
- Ⓐ N-A-M-E.
- Ⓑ M-A-R-I-A.
- Ⓒ I-S-A-B-E-L.
- Ⓓ F-U-E-N-T-E-S.

19. What's your _____ number?
- Ⓐ zip
- Ⓑ security
- Ⓒ e-mail
- Ⓓ telephone

20. My phone number is _____.
- Ⓐ 20018
- Ⓑ 317-29-7834
- Ⓒ (627) 442-3862
- Ⓓ #17-H

21. _____ are you from?
- Ⓐ Where
- Ⓑ When
- Ⓒ Why
- Ⓓ How

22. _____ from Guatemala.
- Ⓐ I
- Ⓑ I'm
- Ⓒ My
- Ⓓ You're

23. What's your _____?
- Ⓐ age
- Ⓑ weight
- Ⓒ height
- Ⓓ nationality

24. I'm five _____ four inches.
- Ⓐ feet
- Ⓑ pounds
- Ⓒ tall
- Ⓓ weigh

....

16 Ⓐ Ⓑ Ⓒ Ⓓ   19 Ⓐ Ⓑ Ⓒ Ⓓ   22 Ⓐ Ⓑ Ⓒ Ⓓ

17 Ⓐ Ⓑ Ⓒ Ⓓ   20 Ⓐ Ⓑ Ⓒ Ⓓ   23 Ⓐ Ⓑ Ⓒ Ⓓ

18 Ⓐ Ⓑ Ⓒ Ⓓ   21 Ⓐ Ⓑ Ⓒ Ⓓ   24 Ⓐ Ⓑ Ⓒ Ⓓ

Go to the next page ⟩

Look at the calendar. Choose the correct answer.

2009

January	February	March	April
May	June	July	August
September	October	November	December

Example:

Today is September 3rd. Today is _____.
- Ⓐ Monday
- Ⓑ Wednesday
- Ⓒ Thursday
- Ⓓ Saturday

Ⓐ ● Ⓒ Ⓓ

25. My birthday is March 13th. This year my birthday is on a _____.
- Ⓐ Monday
- Ⓑ Sunday
- Ⓒ Tuesday
- Ⓓ Thursday

26. My father's birthday is December 22nd. This year his birthday is on a _____.
- Ⓐ Sunday
- Ⓑ Monday
- Ⓒ Wednesday
- Ⓓ Saturday

27. I'm going to start a new job on the first Monday in May. My first day of work is _____.
- Ⓐ May 1st
- Ⓑ May 2nd
- Ⓒ May 5th
- Ⓓ May 26th

28. The twelfth day of March this year is on a _____.
- Ⓐ Wednesday
- Ⓑ Saturday
- Ⓒ Sunday
- Ⓓ Thursday

29. My sister is going to get married on the second Saturday in June. The wedding is on _____.
- Ⓐ June 7th
- Ⓑ June 8th
- Ⓒ June 14th
- Ⓓ June 15th

25 Ⓐ Ⓑ Ⓒ Ⓓ   27 Ⓐ Ⓑ Ⓒ Ⓓ   29 Ⓐ Ⓑ Ⓒ Ⓓ

26 Ⓐ Ⓑ Ⓒ Ⓓ   28 Ⓐ Ⓑ Ⓒ Ⓓ

Go to the next page ➡

Choose the correct answers to complete the story.

There are six people in my family. My father is am are a cashier. He
                                                ●   (B) (C)

work works working ³⁰ in a supermarket. My mother is a an the ³¹ teacher.
(A)   (B)   (C)   (A) (B) (C)

She He It ³² works in a pre-school. My sister is with in from ³³ college. She's
(A) (B) (C)   (A)   (B) (C)

study studies studying ³⁴ medicine. I have two brother brother's brothers ³⁵. One
(A)   (B)   (C)   (A)   (B)   (C)

brother is eight years old. He's in high elementary middle ³⁶ school. The other brother is
                                      (A)   (B)   (C)

sixteen years old. He's in high elementary middle ³⁷ school.
                             (A)   (B)   (C)

Read and listen to the questions. Then listen to the interview and answer the questions.

38. What's his address?
    (A) 19 Reedville Street.
    (B) 94 Reedville Street.
    (C) 419 Center Street.
    (D) 94 Center Street.

39. When is his birthday?
    (A) May 3rd.
    (B) May 13th.
    (C) May 30th.
    (D) May 31st.

40. How tall is he?
    (A) 5 feet 3 inches.
    (B) 8 feet 5 inches.
    (C) 5 feet 8 inches.
    (D) 5 feet 10 inches.

Look at the abbreviation. Write the correct month of the year.

NOV _____November_____   JUL _____   JAN _____

AUG _____   JUN _____   FEB _____

MAR _____   APR _____   MAY _____

SEP _____   OCT _____   DEC _____

Look at the abbreviation. Write the correct day of the week.

MON _____   FRI _____   SUN _____

WED _____   SAT _____   TUE _____

THU _____

Write today's date. _____   **Write your date of birth.** _____

. . . .

30 (A) (B) (C) (D)   **33** (A) (B) (C) (D)   **36** (A) (B) (C) (D)   **39** (A) (B) (C) (D)

31 (A) (B) (C) (D)   **34** (A) (B) (C) (D)   **37** (A) (B) (C) (D)   **40** (A) (B) (C) (D)

32 (A) (B) (C) (D)   **35** (A) (B) (C) (D)   **38** (A) (B) (C) (D)

Go to the next page ⟩

I ORDINAL NUMBERS

Write the correct ordinal number.

second   __2nd__   seventeenth _____

ninth   _____   thirty-first _____

first   _____   fifty-third _____

twelfth   _____   eighty-fifth _____

Write the correct word.

6th _____ __sixth__

15th _____

21st _____

92nd _____

J WRITING ASSESSMENT: Personal Information Form

Fill out the form.

Name: _____

Street: _____ Apartment: _____

City: _____ State: _____ Zip Code: _____

Telephone: _____ E-Mail: _____

Height: _____ Age: _____ Date of Birth: _____ Social Security Number: _____

Hair Color: _____ Eye Color: _____ Country of Origin: _____

Signature: _____ Today's Date: _____

K SPEAKING ASSESSMENT

I can ask and answer these questions:

Ask Answer
- ☐ ☐ What's your name?
- ☐ ☐ What's your address?
- ☐ ☐ What's your telephone number?
- ☐ ☐ What's your age?
- ☐ ☐ What's your date of birth?

Ask Answer
- ☐ ☐ Where are you from?
- ☐ ☐ What's your social security number?
- ☐ ☐ What's your height?
- ☐ ☐ Who are the people in your family?
- ☐ ☐ What do they do?

Name _____

Date _____ Class _____

Choose the correct answer.

Example:

The _____ is in the classroom.
- Ⓐ custodian
- ● teacher
- Ⓒ security officer
- Ⓓ clerk

1. The _____ is in the library.

- Ⓐ principal
- Ⓑ security officer
- Ⓒ librarian
- Ⓓ science teacher

2. Our _____ is in the chemistry lab.

- Ⓐ science teacher
- Ⓑ English teacher
- Ⓒ music teacher
- Ⓓ school nurse

3. The _____ is in her office.

- Ⓐ driver's ed instructor
- Ⓑ librarian
- Ⓒ security officer
- Ⓓ principal

4. The _____ is in the cafeteria.

- Ⓐ music teacher
- Ⓑ custodian
- Ⓒ clerk
- Ⓓ security officer

5. The _____ is on the field.

- Ⓐ principal
- Ⓑ school nurse
- Ⓒ P.E. teacher
- Ⓓ science teacher

6. The _____ is in his office.

- Ⓐ librarian
- Ⓑ school nurse
- Ⓒ clerk
- Ⓓ guidance counselor

7. The _____ is in her classroom.

- Ⓐ music teacher
- Ⓑ English teacher
- Ⓒ science teacher
- Ⓓ P.E. teacher

8. The _____ is in the hall.

- Ⓐ principal
- Ⓑ driver's ed instructor
- Ⓒ security officer
- Ⓓ clerk

9. The _____ is in the parking lot.

- Ⓐ P.E. teacher
- Ⓑ driver's ed instructor
- Ⓒ guidance counselor
- Ⓓ security officer

10. The _____ is in the school office.

- Ⓐ teacher
- Ⓑ school nurse
- Ⓒ security guard
- Ⓓ clerk

11. Our _____ is in our classroom.

- Ⓐ music teacher
- Ⓑ English teacher
- Ⓒ math teacher
- Ⓓ science teacher

....

1 Ⓐ Ⓑ Ⓒ Ⓓ   4 Ⓐ Ⓑ Ⓒ Ⓓ   7 Ⓐ Ⓑ Ⓒ Ⓓ   10 Ⓐ Ⓑ Ⓒ Ⓓ

2 Ⓐ Ⓑ Ⓒ Ⓓ   5 Ⓐ Ⓑ Ⓒ Ⓓ   8 Ⓐ Ⓑ Ⓒ Ⓓ   11 Ⓐ Ⓑ Ⓒ Ⓓ

3 Ⓐ Ⓑ Ⓒ Ⓓ   6 Ⓐ Ⓑ Ⓒ Ⓓ   9 Ⓐ Ⓑ Ⓒ Ⓓ

Go to the next page ▷

B CLASSROOM INSTRUCTIONS

Choose the correct answer.

Example:

Open your _____.
- Ⓐ ruler
- Ⓑ pencil
- Ⓒ wall
- Ⓓ book Ⓐ Ⓑ Ⓒ ⬤

12. Raise your _____.
- Ⓐ seat
- Ⓑ book
- Ⓒ hand
- Ⓓ computer

13. Erase the _____.
- Ⓐ board
- Ⓑ pencil
- Ⓒ pen
- Ⓓ globe

14. Take out a piece of _____.
- Ⓐ map
- Ⓑ dictionary
- Ⓒ book
- Ⓓ paper

15. Please hand in your _____.
- Ⓐ homework
- Ⓑ hand
- Ⓒ chair
- Ⓓ desk

16. Turn off the _____.
- Ⓐ map
- Ⓑ lights
- Ⓒ notebook
- Ⓓ ruler

C COMPUTER COMPONENTS

Look at the picture. Choose the correct word.

17.
- Ⓐ radio
- Ⓑ television
- Ⓒ monitor
- Ⓓ video

18.
- Ⓐ printer
- Ⓑ dictionary
- Ⓒ typewriter
- Ⓓ keyboard

19.
- Ⓐ notebook
- Ⓑ printer
- Ⓒ bookcase
- Ⓓ desk

20.
- Ⓐ mouse
- Ⓑ keyboard
- Ⓒ globe
- Ⓓ map

12 Ⓐ Ⓑ Ⓒ Ⓓ   15 Ⓐ Ⓑ Ⓒ Ⓓ   18 Ⓐ Ⓑ Ⓒ Ⓓ
13 Ⓐ Ⓑ Ⓒ Ⓓ   16 Ⓐ Ⓑ Ⓒ Ⓓ   19 Ⓐ Ⓑ Ⓒ Ⓓ
14 Ⓐ Ⓑ Ⓒ Ⓓ   17 Ⓐ Ⓑ Ⓒ Ⓓ   20 Ⓐ Ⓑ Ⓒ Ⓓ

Go to the next page ▷

D GRAMMAR IN CONTEXT: School Registration

Choose the correct answer to complete the conversation.

21. I want to _____ for an English class.
- Ⓐ teach
- Ⓑ go
- Ⓒ register
- Ⓓ study

22. Okay. Please fill out this _____.
- Ⓐ want ad
- Ⓑ registration form
- Ⓒ job application form
- Ⓓ income tax form

23. With a pen or _____?
- Ⓐ a mouse
- Ⓑ a pencil
- Ⓒ a keyboard
- Ⓓ an eraser

24. A pen. And don't write. Please _____.
- Ⓐ print
- Ⓑ erase
- Ⓒ say
- Ⓓ type

E READING: A Class Schedule

Look at Gloria's class schedule. Choose the correct answer.

Time	Period	Class	Room
8:30–9:15	1st	P.E.	Gym
9:20–10:05	2nd	Math	217
10:10–10:50	3rd	English	115
10:55–11:40	4th	Social Studies	208
12:35–1:20	5th	Health	126
1:25–2:10	6th	Science	130
2:15–3:00	7th	Art	105

Example:

What does she study during fourth period?
- Ⓐ Health.
- Ⓑ Science.
- Ⓒ Social Studies.
- Ⓓ English.   Ⓐ Ⓑ ● Ⓓ

25. What does she study during second period?
- Ⓐ P.E.
- Ⓑ Health.
- Ⓒ Art.
- Ⓓ Math.

26. It's 2:00. What's she studying?
- Ⓐ Social Studies.
- Ⓑ English.
- Ⓒ Science.
- Ⓓ Health.

27. It's 10:30. Where is she?
- Ⓐ In Room 115.
- Ⓑ In the gym.
- Ⓒ In Room 130.
- Ⓓ In Room 105.

28. When does she study in Room 126?
- Ⓐ Third period.
- Ⓑ Fifth perod.
- Ⓒ Sixth period.
- Ⓓ Seventh period.

29. What time does her Science class begin?
- Ⓐ At 8:30.
- Ⓑ At 2:10.
- Ⓒ At 1:25.
- Ⓓ At 1:30.

30. What time does her 7th period class end?
- Ⓐ At 9:15.
- Ⓑ At 2:15.
- Ⓒ In Room 105.
- Ⓓ At 3:00.

··

21 Ⓐ Ⓑ Ⓒ Ⓓ   24 Ⓐ Ⓑ Ⓒ Ⓓ   27 Ⓐ Ⓑ Ⓒ Ⓓ   30 Ⓐ Ⓑ Ⓒ Ⓓ

22 Ⓐ Ⓑ Ⓒ Ⓓ   25 Ⓐ Ⓑ Ⓒ Ⓓ   28 Ⓐ Ⓑ Ⓒ Ⓓ

23 Ⓐ Ⓑ Ⓒ Ⓓ   26 Ⓐ Ⓑ Ⓒ Ⓓ   29 Ⓐ Ⓑ Ⓒ Ⓓ

F CLOZE READING: The Education System

There are many kinds of schools in the education system of the United States. Many young children **go** _goes_ _going_ to pre-school, but other children _stayed_ _stays_ _stay_ [31] home or go to day-care centers. The _one_ _first_ _last_ [32] year of public school for most children is kindergarten. In some school systems, children go _from_ _to_ _with_ [33] kindergarten for a full day. In other school systems, _they_ _we_ _I_ [34] go to school for _half_ _have_ _heavy_ [35] a day. After kindergarten, children usually go to school for 12 _days_ _months_ _years_ [36]. They go to elementary school, middle school, and high school. After that, many students _study_ _studying_ _studies_ [37] in colleges, technical schools, and other institutions.

G LISTENING ASSESSMENT: Registration Procedures

Read and listen to the questions. Then listen to the conversation and answer the questions.

38. When DOESN'T the school have English classes?
    - (A) On Monday.
    - (B) On Friday.
    - (C) On Wednesday.
    - (D) On Saturday.

39. Where is Wendy going to write her personal information?
    - (A) On her driver's license.
    - (B) On a registration form.
    - (C) On a pen.
    - (D) On a short English test.

40. At what time AREN'T there any classes at this school?
    - (A) 10:00 A.M.
    - (B) 7:30 P.M.
    - (C) 2:00 P.M.
    - (D) 11:30 A.M.

H LEARNING SKILLS: Chronological Order & Steps in a Process

Put the classroom instructions in order.

_____ Write the answer.
_____ Sit down.
__1__ Stand up.
_____ Pick up the chalk.
_____ Go to the board.
_____ Put down the chalk.

Put the computer operations in order.

_____ Do your work.
_____ Insert the software disk.
_____ Eject the disk and turn off the computer.
_____ Open the software program.
_____ Save your work and close the program.
__1__ Turn on the computer.

I WRITING ASSESSMENT

Describe your school. Tell about the people, the classrooms, and other locations. (Use a separate sheet of paper.)

J SPEAKING ASSESSMENT

I can ask and answer these questions:

Ask Answer

☐ ☐ Where is our classroom?
☐ ☐ What's our class schedule?

---

31 (A) (B) (C) (D)
32 (A) (B) (C) (D)
33 (A) (B) (C) (D)
34 (A) (B) (C) (D)
35 (A) (B) (C) (D)
36 (A) (B) (C) (D)
37 (A) (B) (C) (D)
38 (A) (B) (C) (D)
39 (A) (B) (C) (D)
40 (A) (B) (C) (D)

STOP

A FOOD CONTAINERS & QUANTITIES

Example: We need a _____ of jam.
- Ⓐ box
- Ⓑ loaf
- ● jar
- Ⓓ bag

1. Please get a _____ of white bread.
- Ⓐ loaf
- Ⓑ bunch
- Ⓒ quart
- Ⓓ bottle

2. I'm looking for a _____ of flour.
- Ⓐ pint
- Ⓑ head
- Ⓒ loaf
- Ⓓ bag

3. I need two _____ of whole wheat bread.
- Ⓐ loaf
- Ⓑ loaves
- Ⓒ heads
- Ⓓ boxes

4. I need a _____ eggs.
- Ⓐ box
- Ⓑ twelve
- Ⓒ dozen
- Ⓓ pound

5. Please give me a _____ of cheese.
- Ⓐ can
- Ⓑ gallon
- Ⓒ pint
- Ⓓ pound

B FOOD WEIGHTS & MEASURES: Abbreviations

6. gal.
- Ⓐ quart
- Ⓑ pound
- Ⓒ gallon
- Ⓓ ounce

7. oz.
- Ⓐ ounce
- Ⓑ quart
- Ⓒ pound
- Ⓓ pounds

8. qt.
- Ⓐ pound
- Ⓑ pounds
- Ⓒ quart
- Ⓓ quarts

9. lbs.
- Ⓐ pound
- Ⓑ pounds
- Ⓒ quart
- Ⓓ quarts

10. ounces
- Ⓐ ozs.
- Ⓑ oz.
- Ⓒ lb.
- Ⓓ lbs.

11. pound
- Ⓐ gal.
- Ⓑ qt.
- Ⓒ lbs.
- Ⓓ lb.

C GRAMMAR IN CONTEXT: Asking About Availability & Location of Items in a Store

12. _____ any bananas today?
- Ⓐ Is there
- Ⓑ Are there
- Ⓒ There is
- Ⓓ There are

13. Yes. _____ in the Produce section.
- Ⓐ It
- Ⓑ It's
- Ⓒ They
- Ⓓ They're

14. Excuse me. _____ the milk?
- Ⓐ Have
- Ⓑ Where
- Ⓒ Where's
- Ⓓ Where are

15. _____ in the Dairy section.
- Ⓐ It's
- Ⓑ It
- Ⓒ They're
- Ⓓ They

1 Ⓐ Ⓑ Ⓒ Ⓓ   5 Ⓐ Ⓑ Ⓒ Ⓓ   9 Ⓐ Ⓑ Ⓒ Ⓓ   13 Ⓐ Ⓑ Ⓒ Ⓓ

2 Ⓐ Ⓑ Ⓒ Ⓓ   6 Ⓐ Ⓑ Ⓒ Ⓓ   10 Ⓐ Ⓑ Ⓒ Ⓓ   14 Ⓐ Ⓑ Ⓒ Ⓓ

3 Ⓐ Ⓑ Ⓒ Ⓓ   7 Ⓐ Ⓑ Ⓒ Ⓓ   11 Ⓐ Ⓑ Ⓒ Ⓓ   15 Ⓐ Ⓑ Ⓒ Ⓓ

4 Ⓐ Ⓑ Ⓒ Ⓓ   8 Ⓐ Ⓑ Ⓒ Ⓓ   12 Ⓐ Ⓑ Ⓒ Ⓓ

Look at the food advertisements. Choose the correct answer.

16. How much are four heads of lettuce?
- (A) $2.00.
- (B) $3.00.
- (C) $4.00.
- (D) $8.00.

17. How much is half a pound of Swiss cheese?
- (A) $17.00.
- (B) $2.50.
- (C) $4.25.
- (D) $8.50.

18. How much are two pounds of Swiss cheese?
- (A) $8.50.
- (B) $17.00.
- (C) $4.25.
- (D) $2.00.

19. How much are four oranges?
- (A) $2.00.
- (B) $1.00.
- (C) $8.00.
- (D) $4.00.

20. How much are a dozen oranges?
- (A) $1.00.
- (B) $2.00.
- (C) $6.00.
- (D) $12.00.

21. How much are two bottles of apple juice?
- (A) Free.
- (B) $1.75.
- (C) $6.98.
- (D) $3.49.

16 (A) (B) (C) (D)   18 (A) (B) (C) (D)   20 (A) (B) (C) (D)

17 (A) (B) (C) (D)   19 (A) (B) (C) (D)   21 (A) (B) (C) (D)

Go to the next page ⟩

E READING: Food Packaging & Label Information

For each sentence, choose the correct label.

A	B	C	D
SELL BY MAR 04	Keep Refrigerated	Serving Size 1 cup (240g) Servings Per Container about 2	Center Pops Up When Original Seal Is Broken

22. Do not store at room temperature.
    Ⓐ Ⓑ Ⓒ Ⓓ

23. Contains 2 cups (480g).
    Ⓐ Ⓑ Ⓒ Ⓓ

24. Do not purchase if safety button is up.
    Ⓐ Ⓑ Ⓒ Ⓓ

25. Do not buy after this date.
    Ⓐ Ⓑ Ⓒ Ⓓ

F READING: A Supermarket Receipt

Look at the receipt. Choose the correct answer.

26. How much did the eggs cost?
    Ⓐ $2.69.   Ⓒ $2.10.
    Ⓑ $2.00.   Ⓓ $3.00.

27. How many bottles of soda did the person buy?
    Ⓐ One.   Ⓒ Three.
    Ⓑ Two.   Ⓓ Four.

28. How much did the person spend on soda?
    Ⓐ $2.00.   Ⓒ $1.00.
    Ⓑ $3.00.   Ⓓ $6.00.

29. How much does one loaf of bread cost?
    Ⓐ $1.00.   Ⓒ $3.00.
    Ⓑ $2.00.   Ⓓ $6.00.

30. How much do oranges cost at this supermarket?
    Ⓐ $3.00.   Ⓒ 12 for $4.00.
    Ⓑ 3 for $4.00.   Ⓓ 4 for $1.00.

31. How much did the person spend?
    Ⓐ $473.00.   Ⓒ $22.04.
    Ⓑ $2.96.   Ⓓ $25.00.

```
        JUMBO SUPERMARKET #473

        LARGE EGGS          2.10
        MILK                2.69
        JAM                 3.25
      2 @ $1.00
        SODA                2.00
      3 @ $2.00
        BREAD               6.00
      2 @ 2 for $3.00
        LETTUCE             3.00
      12 @ 4 for $1.00
        ORANGES             3.00

           TOTAL        $ 22.04
           TENDER       $ 25.00
           CHANGE       $  2.96

      Thanks for shopping at JUMBO!
```

22 Ⓐ Ⓑ Ⓒ Ⓓ   25 Ⓐ Ⓑ Ⓒ Ⓓ   28 Ⓐ Ⓑ Ⓒ Ⓓ   31 Ⓐ Ⓑ Ⓒ Ⓓ

23 Ⓐ Ⓑ Ⓒ Ⓓ   26 Ⓐ Ⓑ Ⓒ Ⓓ   29 Ⓐ Ⓑ Ⓒ Ⓓ

24 Ⓐ Ⓑ Ⓒ Ⓓ   27 Ⓐ Ⓑ Ⓒ Ⓓ   30 Ⓐ Ⓑ Ⓒ Ⓓ

Go to the next page ➤

Look at the menu. Choose the correct answer.

SAMMY'S CAFE

SOUP

Vegetable Soup	Cup	1.50	Bowl	2.50
Onion Soup		2.00		3.00

SALAD

Tossed Salad   Small   1.50   Large   3.00

SIDE DISHES

French Fries	2.50	Carrots	2.00
Rice	3.00	Peas	2.00

ENTREES

Chicken	7.00	Spaghetti &	
Fish	8.00	Meatballs	6.50
Steak	10.00	Vegetable Stew	7.50

DESSERTS

Pie	3.50	Fresh Strawberries	4.00
Cake	3.50		

32. Julia ate at Sammy's Cafe yesterday. She ordered a bowl of vegetable soup and a large salad. How much did she pay?
- Ⓐ $3.00.
- Ⓑ $4.00.
- Ⓒ $5.50.
- Ⓓ $6.00.

33. Ken ordered a small salad, chicken, and rice. How much did he spend?
- Ⓐ $11.50.
- Ⓑ $12.00.
- Ⓒ $12.50.
- Ⓓ $13.00.

34. Sally ate a cup of onion soup, fish, and peas. How much was her bill?
- Ⓐ $11.50.
- Ⓑ $12.50.
- Ⓒ $13.00.
- Ⓓ $12.00.

35. Jeff had a cup of vegetable soup, steak, french fries, and carrots. How much did he spend at the restaurant?
- Ⓐ $16.00.
- Ⓑ $15.50.
- Ⓒ $15.00.
- Ⓓ $14.50.

36. Dora ordered a small salad, vegetable stew, and a piece of cake for dessert. What did she pay?
- Ⓐ $11.50.
- Ⓑ $12.00.
- Ⓒ $12.50.
- Ⓓ $13.00.

37. Ted ordered a bowl of onion soup, chicken, carrots, peas, and fresh strawberries. How much did he pay?
- Ⓐ $16.00.
- Ⓑ $18.00.
- Ⓒ $17.00.
- Ⓓ $17.50.

H   LISTENING ASSESSMENT: Ordering a Meal

Read and listen to the questions. Then listen to the conversation and answer the questions.

38. Where is the conversation taking place?
- Ⓐ In a supermarket.
- Ⓑ In a restaurant.
- Ⓒ In a home.
- Ⓓ In a school lunchroom.

39. What is the customer going to have for an appetizer?
- Ⓐ A glass of milk.
- Ⓑ An order of rice.
- Ⓒ The baked chicken.
- Ⓓ A bowl of soup.

40. How many side orders is the customer going to have?
- Ⓐ None.
- Ⓑ One.
- Ⓒ Two.
- Ⓓ Three.

I   WRITING ASSESSMENT

What do you usually buy at the supermarket or other food store? How much do you usually spend? Write about it on a separate sheet of paper.

J   SPEAKING ASSESSMENT

I can ask and answer these questions:

Ask Answer
- ☐ ☐   What foods do you like?
- ☐ ☐   What did you have for breakfast today?
- ☐ ☐   What did you have for dinner yesterday?

A SMALL TALK AT WORK & AT SCHOOL

Choose the correct response.

1. What time is the break?
   - (A) It's on Friday.
   - (B) Every morning.
   - (C) It's at 10:30.
   - (D) Five days a week.

2. What's the weather forecast for tomorrow?
   - (A) It's raining.
   - (B) It's going to rain.
   - (C) It rained.
   - (D) It didn't rain.

3. I'm really tired today.
   - (A) Congratulations!
   - (B) That's great!
   - (C) I'm glad to hear that.
   - (D) I'm sorry to hear that.

4. It's very hot in the building today.
   - (A) I agree. It's hot.
   - (B) I agree. It isn't very hot.
   - (C) I disagree. It's hot.
   - (D) I disagree. It's very hot.

5. What kind of TV shows do you like?
   - (A) You like news programs.
   - (B) I like news programs.
   - (C) I play baseball.
   - (D) I like adventure movies.

6. Did you see the president on TV last night?
   - (A) No, he wasn't.
   - (B) No, you didn't.
   - (C) Yes, I did.
   - (D) Yes, you did.

7. Do you think Mr. Lawson will give a math test tomorrow?
   - (A) I agree.
   - (B) I disagree.
   - (C) I think she will.
   - (D) I think he will.

8. Do you think it'll rain tomorrow?
   - (A) Maybe it will, and maybe it won't.
   - (B) Maybe we will, and maybe we won't.
   - (C) Maybe you will, and maybe you won't.
   - (D) Maybe I will, and maybe I won't.

9. Do you think we'll have to work overtime?
   - (A) Maybe we did, and maybe we didn't.
   - (B) Maybe we do, and maybe we don't.
   - (C) Maybe we will, and maybe we won't.
   - (D) Maybe we are, and maybe we aren't.

10. Are you going out for lunch today?
   - (A) No. I'm going to a restaurant.
   - (B) No. I'm going to eat in my office.
   - (C) Yes. I'm going to eat in my office.
   - (D) Yes. I'm not going out for lunch.

----

1 (A) (B) (C) (D)   4 (A) (B) (C) (D)   7 (A) (B) (C) (D)   10 (A) (B) (C) (D)

2 (A) (B) (C) (D)   5 (A) (B) (C) (D)   8 (A) (B) (C) (D)

3 (A) (B) (C) (D)   6 (A) (B) (C) (D)   9 (A) (B) (C) (D)

B GRAMMAR IN CONTEXT: Invitations & Offers

Choose the correct answer to complete the conversations.

11. Would _____ like some milk?
- Ⓐ you'll
- Ⓑ you
- Ⓒ you're
- Ⓓ you do

12. _____ I'd love some.
- Ⓐ Yes. Thanks.
- Ⓑ No. Thanks.
- Ⓒ No thank you.
- Ⓓ Please don't.

13. Would you like to _____ with me after work today?
- Ⓐ will have dinner
- Ⓑ has dinner
- Ⓒ having dinner
- Ⓓ have dinner

14. I'm sorry. _____
- Ⓐ You can't.
- Ⓑ You can.
- Ⓒ I can't.
- Ⓓ I can.

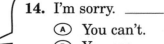

15. _____ you sure?
- Ⓐ Do
- Ⓑ Does
- Ⓒ Is
- Ⓓ Are

16. Yes. _____ work late.
- Ⓐ I have to
- Ⓑ I have
- Ⓒ You have
- Ⓓ I'm

17. _____ like to go sailing with me?
- Ⓐ Did you
- Ⓑ Did I
- Ⓒ Would you
- Ⓓ Would I

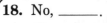

18. No, _____.
- Ⓐ I don't
- Ⓑ I don't think so
- Ⓒ I think so
- Ⓓ I think

19. Why _____?
- Ⓐ don't
- Ⓑ doesn't
- Ⓒ no
- Ⓓ not

20. _____ get seasick.
- Ⓐ He might
- Ⓑ I'm
- Ⓒ I'm afraid I might
- Ⓓ You're afraid

....

11 Ⓐ Ⓑ Ⓒ Ⓓ   14 Ⓐ Ⓑ Ⓒ Ⓓ   17 Ⓐ Ⓑ Ⓒ Ⓓ   20 Ⓐ Ⓑ Ⓒ Ⓓ

12 Ⓐ Ⓑ Ⓒ Ⓓ   15 Ⓐ Ⓑ Ⓒ Ⓓ   18 Ⓐ Ⓑ Ⓒ Ⓓ

13 Ⓐ Ⓑ Ⓒ Ⓓ   16 Ⓐ Ⓑ Ⓒ Ⓓ   19 Ⓐ Ⓑ Ⓒ Ⓓ

Go to the next page ⟶

Choose the correct answer to complete the conversations.

21. Will the train _____ soon?
- Ⓐ will arrive
- Ⓑ arrive
- Ⓒ going to arrive
- Ⓓ is going to arrive

22. Yes. _____ in five minutes.
- Ⓐ Arrive
- Ⓑ Going to arrive
- Ⓒ It arrive
- Ⓓ It'll arrive

23. _____
- Ⓐ In five minutes?
- Ⓑ It'll arrive?
- Ⓒ Yes, it will.
- Ⓓ No?

24. Yes. _____
- Ⓐ It's going to.
- Ⓑ You'll arrive.
- Ⓒ I will.
- Ⓓ That's right.

25. My birthday is _____ May 3rd.
- Ⓐ from
- Ⓑ with
- Ⓒ on
- Ⓓ at

26. May _____?
- Ⓐ who
- Ⓑ what
- Ⓒ why
- Ⓓ how

27. Where _____ you live?
- Ⓐ do
- Ⓑ does
- Ⓒ is
- Ⓓ are

28. I live _____ apartment 3-C.
- Ⓐ on
- Ⓑ with
- Ⓒ for
- Ⓓ in

29. _____ 3-G?
- Ⓐ Did you live
- Ⓑ Do you live
- Ⓒ Did you say
- Ⓓ Do you say

30. _____
- Ⓐ Yes. 3-G.
- Ⓑ Yes. 3-C.
- Ⓒ No. 3-G.
- Ⓓ No. 3-C.

21 Ⓐ Ⓑ Ⓒ Ⓓ   24 Ⓐ Ⓑ Ⓒ Ⓓ   27 Ⓐ Ⓑ Ⓒ Ⓓ   30 Ⓐ Ⓑ Ⓒ Ⓓ

22 Ⓐ Ⓑ Ⓒ Ⓓ   25 Ⓐ Ⓑ Ⓒ Ⓓ   28 Ⓐ Ⓑ Ⓒ Ⓓ

23 Ⓐ Ⓑ Ⓒ Ⓓ   26 Ⓐ Ⓑ Ⓒ Ⓓ   29 Ⓐ Ⓑ Ⓒ Ⓓ

Go to the next page ▷

D CLOZE READING: Small Talk at Work

Choose the correct answers to complete the story.

"Small talk" [of (A)] [at (●)] [when (C)] [31] work is very important. Co-workers [talk (A)] [talks (B)] [talking (C)] [31] with each other about many different things. They talk about [my (A)] [your (B)] [their (C)] [32] favorite movies and TV programs. They talk [above (A)] [about (B)] [with (C)] [33] music and sports. [Much (A)] [Many (B)] [Co-workers (C)] [34] people also talk about the weather. Some subjects [don't (A)] [aren't (B)] [isn't (C)] [35] very good for "small talk" in some countries, but in other countries [this (A)] [that (B)] [these (C)] [36] subjects are very common. For example, questions about a person's salary or the [price (A)] [receipt (B)] [how much (C)] [37] of a person's home are common in some countries but very unusual in other countries.

E LISTENING ASSESSMENT: An Invitation

Read and listen to the questions. Then listen to the conversation and answer the questions.

38. What day is it?
    - (A) Tuesday.
    - (B) Wednesday.
    - (C) Thursday.
    - (D) We don't know.

39. What are they going to do tomorrow?
    - (A) Make dinner.
    - (B) Have dinner.
    - (C) Go to a class.
    - (D) Go to a meeting.

40. Where are they going to meet?
    - (A) At the restaurant.
    - (B) At the computer class.
    - (C) On Wednesday.
    - (D) At the person's office.

F WRITING ASSESSMENT

Describe your plans for the weekend. What are you going to do? What might you do? Write about it on a separate sheet of paper.

G SPEAKING ASSESSMENT

I can ask and answer these questions:

Ask Answer
- ☐ ☐ How do you like the weather today?
- ☐ ☐ What's the weather forecast for tomorrow?
- ☐ ☐ What kind of TV shows do you like?
- ☐ ☐ What kind of music do you like?
- ☐ ☐ What did you do last weekend?
- ☐ ☐ What are you going to do next weekend?

---

31 (A) (B) (C) (D)   34 (A) (B) (C) (D)   37 (A) (B) (C) (D)   40 (A) (B) (C) (D)

32 (A) (B) (C) (D)   35 (A) (B) (C) (D)   38 (A) (B) (C) (D)

33 (A) (B) (C) (D)   36 (A) (B) (C) (D)   39 (A) (B) (C) (D)

STOP

A SMALL TALK AT WORK & AT SCHOOL

Choose the correct response.

1. How do you like our new boss?
   I think she's _____ our old boss.
   - Ⓐ friendly
   - Ⓑ friendlier
   - Ⓒ friendlier than
   - Ⓓ more friendly

2. What do you think about our new English
   teacher?
   I think he's _____ our old teacher.
   - Ⓐ nicer
   - Ⓑ nicer than
   - Ⓒ more nice than
   - Ⓓ more nice

3. What's your favorite kind of music?
   Rock music. I think it's _____ other kinds
   of music.
   - Ⓐ better than
   - Ⓑ good than
   - Ⓒ more good than
   - Ⓓ more better than

4. The weather today is beautiful.
   I agree. It's _____ yesterday.
   - Ⓐ nice
   - Ⓑ nicer
   - Ⓒ nicer than
   - Ⓓ more nice than

5. I think your computer is newer than
   mine.
   It is. Mine is newer than _____.
   - Ⓐ my
   - Ⓑ mine
   - Ⓒ your
   - Ⓓ yours

6. Our math class isn't very interesting any
   more.
   I agree. It _____ more interesting.
   - Ⓐ to be used
   - Ⓑ used to be
   - Ⓒ used be to
   - Ⓓ was to be

7. Should I work overtime today or
   tomorrow?
   _____ work overtime today.
   - Ⓐ You think I should
   - Ⓑ You should I think
   - Ⓒ I think you should
   - Ⓓ I should you think

8. My locker isn't as clean as your locker.
   You're right. Mine _____ yours.
   - Ⓐ is cleaner than
   - Ⓑ isn't cleaner than
   - Ⓒ is as clean as
   - Ⓓ isn't as clean as

9. You know, the food in the cafeteria isn't as
   good as it used to be.
   I agree. The food _____.
   - Ⓐ is better now
   - Ⓑ are better now
   - Ⓒ used to be
   - Ⓓ used to be better

10. I think our science class is more
    interesting than our history class.
    I disagree. I think history _____ science.
    - Ⓐ isn't as interesting
    - Ⓑ isn't as interesting as
    - Ⓒ is more interesting
    - Ⓓ is more interesting than

1 Ⓐ Ⓑ Ⓒ Ⓓ   4 Ⓐ Ⓑ Ⓒ Ⓓ   7 Ⓐ Ⓑ Ⓒ Ⓓ   10 Ⓐ Ⓑ Ⓒ Ⓓ

2 Ⓐ Ⓑ Ⓒ Ⓓ   5 Ⓐ Ⓑ Ⓒ Ⓓ   8 Ⓐ Ⓑ Ⓒ Ⓓ

3 Ⓐ Ⓑ Ⓒ Ⓓ   6 Ⓐ Ⓑ Ⓒ Ⓓ   9 Ⓐ Ⓑ Ⓒ Ⓓ

Go to the next page ▷

B GRAMMAR IN CONTEXT: Compliments

Choose the correct answer to complete the conversations.

11. _____ a very nice bicycle.
- Ⓐ That
- Ⓑ That's
- Ⓒ This
- Ⓓ These

12. _____
- Ⓐ It is that.
- Ⓑ It's a bicycle.
- Ⓒ Thanks.
- Ⓓ You're welcome.

13. _____ fast?
- Ⓐ Is it
- Ⓑ It is
- Ⓒ Are they
- Ⓓ They are

14. Yes. It's _____ my old bicycle.
- Ⓐ faster
- Ⓑ faster than
- Ⓒ more fast
- Ⓓ more

15. These cookies _____.
- Ⓐ is delicious
- Ⓑ more delicious
- Ⓒ much more delicious
- Ⓓ are delicious

16. Thanks. My new recipe is _____ my old one.
- Ⓐ much better than
- Ⓑ much better
- Ⓒ more good
- Ⓓ better

17. Your apartment _____.
- Ⓐ nicer than
- Ⓑ is nicer than
- Ⓒ is very nice
- Ⓓ are very nice

18. Thank you. Do you like _____?
- Ⓐ my sofa is new
- Ⓑ my sofa is newer
- Ⓒ my new sofa
- Ⓓ newer sofa

19. Yes. It's _____ than your old one.
- Ⓐ attractive
- Ⓑ more attractive
- Ⓒ much attractive
- Ⓓ much more

20. I think so, too. It's also _____ comfortable.
- Ⓐ much
- Ⓑ good
- Ⓒ better
- Ⓓ more

11 Ⓐ Ⓑ Ⓒ Ⓓ   14 Ⓐ Ⓑ Ⓒ Ⓓ   17 Ⓐ Ⓑ Ⓒ Ⓓ   20 Ⓐ Ⓑ Ⓒ Ⓓ

12 Ⓐ Ⓑ Ⓒ Ⓓ   15 Ⓐ Ⓑ Ⓒ Ⓓ   18 Ⓐ Ⓑ Ⓒ Ⓓ

13 Ⓐ Ⓑ Ⓒ Ⓓ   16 Ⓐ Ⓑ Ⓒ Ⓓ   19 Ⓐ Ⓑ Ⓒ Ⓓ

Go to the next page ⟶

C GRAMMAR IN CONTEXT: Appropriate Language in Social Situations

Choose the correct answer to complete the conversations.

21. _____ You're stepping on my foot.
- Ⓐ Excuse me.
- Ⓑ Excuse.
- Ⓒ You excuse me.
- Ⓓ I excuse you.

22. Oh. _____
- Ⓐ You apologize.
- Ⓑ I apologize.
- Ⓒ You're apologizing.
- Ⓓ I'm apologizing.

23. That's okay. _____
- Ⓐ Think.
- Ⓑ Don't think.
- Ⓒ Worry about it.
- Ⓓ Don't worry about it.

24. _____
- Ⓐ It's very sorry.
- Ⓑ We're very sorry.
- Ⓒ I'm really sorry.
- Ⓓ You're really sorry.

25. You _____. Is something wrong?
- Ⓐ are looking
- Ⓑ look sad
- Ⓒ sad
- Ⓓ the matter

26. Yes. I have _____.
- Ⓐ some bad news
- Ⓑ some bad
- Ⓒ some good news
- Ⓓ some good

27. What _____?
- Ⓐ happen
- Ⓑ happened
- Ⓒ happening
- Ⓓ going to happen

28. My husband _____ yesterday.
- Ⓐ lose job
- Ⓑ lost job
- Ⓒ lose his job
- Ⓓ lost his job

29. I'm _____ that.
- Ⓐ sorry
- Ⓑ sorry to
- Ⓒ sorry to hear
- Ⓓ sorry hear

30. _____
- Ⓐ Thank you.
- Ⓑ I agree.
- Ⓒ I disagree.
- Ⓓ You're sorry.

....

21 Ⓐ Ⓑ Ⓒ Ⓓ   24 Ⓐ Ⓑ Ⓒ Ⓓ   27 Ⓐ Ⓑ Ⓒ Ⓓ   30 Ⓐ Ⓑ Ⓒ Ⓓ

22 Ⓐ Ⓑ Ⓒ Ⓓ   25 Ⓐ Ⓑ Ⓒ Ⓓ   28 Ⓐ Ⓑ Ⓒ Ⓓ

23 Ⓐ Ⓑ Ⓒ Ⓓ   26 Ⓐ Ⓑ Ⓒ Ⓓ   29 Ⓐ Ⓑ Ⓒ Ⓓ

Go to the next page ⟩

D CLOZE READING: A Thank-You Note

Choose the correct answers to complete the note.

Dear Alan,

Thank you [with (A) / for (●) / by (C)] the wonderful dinner yesterday. [They (A) / It (B) / I (C)] ³¹ was

delicious. The vegetable soup [were (A) / was (B) / did (C)] ³² great, the hamburgers [were (A) / was (B) / are (C)] ³³

excellent, and the [potatoes (A) / carrots (B) / chili (C)] ³⁴ was also very good. In fact, I think your recipe

is much [good (A) / more good (B) / better (C)] ³⁵ than [my (A) / mine (B) / me (C)] ³⁶.

Thank you again. Next time [I'll (A) / I'm (B) / I (C)] ³⁷ invite you to MY place for dinner.

Sincerely,

Natalie

E LISTENING ASSESSMENT: Expressing Opinions

Read and listen to the questions. Then listen to the conversation and answer the questions.

38. What do they disagree about?
    - (A) The buildings.
    - (B) The streets.
    - (C) The people.
    - (D) The weather.

39. What do they agree about?
    - (A) The people and the buildings.
    - (B) The buildings and the parks.
    - (C) The streets and the buildings.
    - (D) The streets and the people.

40. Which opinion do they probably agree about?
    - (A) The buildings in other cities are more interesting.
    - (B) The people in other cities are friendlier.
    - (C) The streets in other cities are cleaner.
    - (D) The parks in other cities are more beautiful.

F WRITING ASSESSMENT

Compare two different places you know. Write about the streets, the buildings, the weather, the people, and life in these two places. (Use a separate sheet of paper.)

G SPEAKING ASSESSMENT

I can ask and answer these questions:

Ask Answer
- ☐ ☐ What's your favorite food?
- ☐ ☐ How do you like my new _____?
- ☐ ☐ What do you think about our English class?
- ☐ ☐ What's your opinion about life in our city?

31 (A) (B) (C) (D)   34 (A) (B) (C) (D)   37 (A) (B) (C) (D)   40 (A) (B) (C) (D)

32 (A) (B) (C) (D)   35 (A) (B) (C) (D)   38 (A) (B) (C) (D)

33 (A) (B) (C) (D)   36 (A) (B) (C) (D)   39 (A) (B) (C) (D)

STOP

A SHOPPING REQUESTS & LOCATING ITEMS

**These people are shopping in a department store. Where is each person shopping?
Choose the correct department.**

Ex: "I'm looking for a new TV."
- Ⓐ Appliances
- ● Home Entertainment
- Ⓑ Jewelry
- Ⓓ Customer Service

1. "Do you have this tie in blue?"
- Ⓐ Jewelry
- Ⓒ Men's Clothing
- Ⓑ Furniture
- Ⓓ Women's Clothing

2. "Is this dishwasher the best one you have?"
- Ⓐ Furniture
- Ⓒ Customer Service
- Ⓑ Appliances
- Ⓓ Home Entertainment

3. "I want to buy a ring."
- Ⓐ Jewelry
- Ⓒ Home Entertainment
- Ⓑ Furniture
- Ⓓ Appliances

4. "We need a new kitchen table."
- Ⓐ Furniture
- Ⓒ Cosmetics
- Ⓑ Jewelry
- Ⓓ Appliances

5. "Do you have any longer dresses?"
- Ⓐ Jewelry
- Ⓒ Women's Clothing
- Ⓑ Furniture
- Ⓓ Home Entertainment

6. "I want to return this item."
- Ⓐ Rest Rooms
- Ⓒ Appliances
- Ⓑ Cosmetics
- Ⓓ Customer Service

7. "I'm looking for a shirt for my little boy."
- Ⓐ Toys
- Ⓒ Men's Clothing
- Ⓑ Appliances
- Ⓓ Children's Clothing

B UNDERSTANDING ATM INSTRUCTIONS

Read the ATM instruction. Choose the correct answer.

8. Enter the amount in dollars and cents.
- Ⓐ OKAY
- Ⓑ 4761
- Ⓒ $50.00
- Ⓓ ENTER

9. Choose a transaction: WITHDRAWAL
- Ⓐ Insert card.
- Ⓑ Get money.
- Ⓒ Put in money.
- Ⓓ Press ENTER.

10. Choose a transaction: DEPOSIT
- Ⓐ Put in money.
- Ⓑ Press OKAY.
- Ⓒ Get money.
- Ⓓ Insert card.

11. Enter your PIN (Personal Identification Number).
- Ⓐ $0.00
- Ⓑ $50.00
- Ⓒ 4761
- Ⓓ P-I-N

12. Balance Inquiry
- Ⓐ Choose another account.
- Ⓑ Last Deposit: $463.12
- Ⓒ Last Withdrawal: $100.00
- Ⓓ Funds available: $1,241.63

13. Do you want to make another transaction?
- Ⓐ Enter your PIN.
- Ⓑ Press YES or NO.
- Ⓒ Enter the amount.
- Ⓓ Insert your card.

....

1 Ⓐ Ⓑ Ⓒ Ⓓ   4 Ⓐ Ⓑ Ⓒ Ⓓ   7 Ⓐ Ⓑ Ⓒ Ⓓ   11 Ⓐ Ⓑ Ⓒ Ⓓ

2 Ⓐ Ⓑ Ⓒ Ⓓ   5 Ⓐ Ⓑ Ⓒ Ⓓ   8 Ⓐ Ⓑ Ⓒ Ⓓ   12 Ⓐ Ⓑ Ⓒ Ⓓ

3 Ⓐ Ⓑ Ⓒ Ⓓ   6 Ⓐ Ⓑ Ⓒ Ⓓ   9 Ⓐ Ⓑ Ⓒ Ⓓ   13 Ⓐ Ⓑ Ⓒ Ⓓ   **Go to the next page** ⟩

10 Ⓐ Ⓑ Ⓒ Ⓓ

C INTERPRETING A CHECK

```
                                                    1024
                                        (1) _____
Pay to the
order of  (2) _____  $ (3) _____

(4) _____ Dollars

For (5) _____   (6) _____

057009345  200042534  1024
```

Look at the information. Where should you write it? Choose the correct line on the check.

14. Savemax Clothing Store
   (A) Line 2   (C) Line 5
   (B) Line 4   (D) Line 6

15. 36.40
   (A) Line 1   (C) Line 4
   (B) Line 3   (D) Line 6

16. Nov. 22, 2009
   (A) Line 1   (C) Line 5
   (B) Line 3   (D) Line 6

17. pants & belt
   (A) Line 2   (C) Line 5
   (B) Line 4   (D) Line 6

18. *Pedro Martinez*
   (A) Line 3   (C) Line 5
   (B) Line 4   (D) Line 6

19. Thirty-six and 40/100..................................
   (A) Line 2   (C) Line 4
   (B) Line 3   (D) Line 5

D GRAMMAR IN CONTEXT: Problems with Purchases; Returning an Item

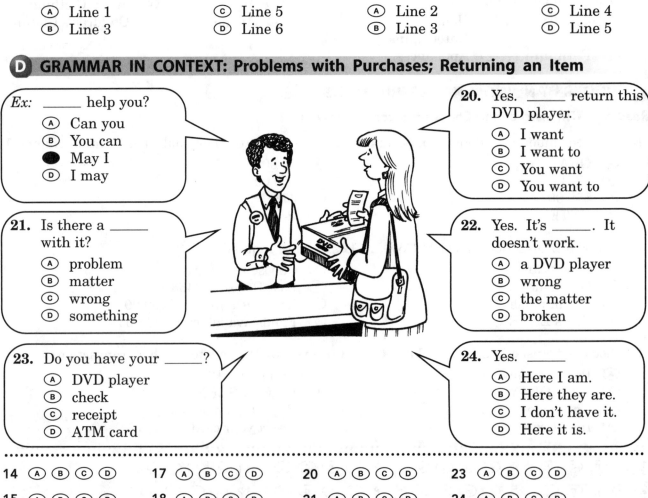

Ex: _____ help you?
  (A) Can you
  (B) You can
  ● May I
  (D) I may

20. Yes. _____ return this DVD player.
  (A) I want
  (B) I want to
  (C) You want
  (D) You want to

21. Is there a _____ with it?
  (A) problem
  (B) matter
  (C) wrong
  (D) something

22. Yes. It's _____. It doesn't work.
  (A) a DVD player
  (B) wrong
  (C) the matter
  (D) broken

23. Do you have your _____?
  (A) DVD player
  (B) check
  (C) receipt
  (D) ATM card

24. Yes. _____
  (A) Here I am.
  (B) Here they are.
  (C) I don't have it.
  (D) Here it is.

14 (A) (B) (C) (D)   17 (A) (B) (C) (D)   20 (A) (B) (C) (D)   23 (A) (B) (C) (D)

15 (A) (B) (C) (D)   18 (A) (B) (C) (D)   21 (A) (B) (C) (D)   24 (A) (B) (C) (D)

16 (A) (B) (C) (D)   19 (A) (B) (C) (D)   22 (A) (B) (C) (D)

Go to the next page ▷

E GRAMMAR IN CONTEXT: Problems with Purchases; Exchanging an Item

25. I'd like to _____ this cell phone.
- Ⓐ give
- Ⓑ return
- Ⓒ take
- Ⓓ call

26. What's the _____ with it?
- Ⓐ matter
- Ⓑ wrong
- Ⓒ why
- Ⓓ what's wrong

27. _____ small enough.
- Ⓐ They aren't
- Ⓑ Aren't they
- Ⓒ It isn't
- Ⓓ Isn't it

28. Do you want to _____ it for a smaller one?
- Ⓐ return
- Ⓑ buy
- Ⓒ give
- Ⓓ exchange

29. _____ a smaller one?
- Ⓐ You do have
- Ⓑ Do you have
- Ⓒ Have you
- Ⓓ You do

30. Yes. This used to be the _____ one, but now we have a smaller one.
- Ⓐ smallest
- Ⓑ more small
- Ⓒ more smallest
- Ⓓ much small

31. Then I think _____ exchange it.
- Ⓐ I like
- Ⓑ you like
- Ⓒ you'd like to
- Ⓓ I'd like to

32. Okay. Go to the Electronics _____. Somebody there will help you.
- Ⓐ store
- Ⓑ furniture
- Ⓒ department
- Ⓓ entertainment

F CLOZE READING: Store Sales

Choose the correct answers to complete the story.

Many department stores [has Ⓐ | have ● | does Ⓒ] sales. When there is a sale, you can

[give Ⓐ | take Ⓑ | buy Ⓒ] ³³ items at special low [prices Ⓐ | receipts Ⓑ | departments Ⓒ] ³⁴. Sometimes you

need a coupon for a sale. You can find coupons in the [radio Ⓐ | newspaper Ⓑ | TV Ⓒ] ³⁵. Many

stores send ads with coupons to people's homes through the [store Ⓐ | mail Ⓑ | service Ⓒ] ³⁶.

Look for sales at stores [near Ⓐ | with Ⓑ | far Ⓒ] ³⁷ you. You can save a lot of money!

••

25 Ⓐ Ⓑ Ⓒ Ⓓ   **29** Ⓐ Ⓑ Ⓒ Ⓓ   **33** Ⓐ Ⓑ Ⓒ Ⓓ   **37** Ⓐ Ⓑ Ⓒ Ⓓ

26 Ⓐ Ⓑ Ⓒ Ⓓ   **30** Ⓐ Ⓑ Ⓒ Ⓓ   **34** Ⓐ Ⓑ Ⓒ Ⓓ

27 Ⓐ Ⓑ Ⓒ Ⓓ   **31** Ⓐ Ⓑ Ⓒ Ⓓ   **35** Ⓐ Ⓑ Ⓒ Ⓓ

28 Ⓐ Ⓑ Ⓒ Ⓓ   **32** Ⓐ Ⓑ Ⓒ Ⓓ   **36** Ⓐ Ⓑ Ⓒ Ⓓ

Read and listen to the questions. Then listen to the conversation and answer the questions.

38. How many items does the person want to return?
Ⓐ One.
Ⓑ Two.
Ⓒ Three.
Ⓓ Four.

39. What's the matter with the shirt?
Ⓐ It's big.
Ⓑ It's large.
Ⓒ It's small.
Ⓓ It's blue.

40. Where is the conversation taking place?
Ⓐ In the elevator.
Ⓑ At the Customer Service Counter.
Ⓒ On the first floor.
Ⓓ In the Men's Clothing Department.

H **WRITING ASSESSMENT: Fill Out the Check**

Pay this bill. Fill out the check.

Metrovision

Cable TV Service	$24.95
Past Due	0.00
DUE NOW	**$24.95**

1024

Pay to the
order of _____ $_____

_____ Dollars

For _____   _____

057009345 200042534 1024

I **LEARNING SKILL: Steps in a Process**

Put the ATM instructions in order.

_____ Choose a transaction.
_____ Take your money, your card, and your receipt.
__1__ Insert your ATM card.
_____ Enter the amount in dollars and cents.
_____ Enter your PIN on the keypad and press ENTER.
_____ Check the amount and press OKAY.

J **SPEAKING ASSESSMENT**

I can ask and answer these questions:

Ask Answer
☐ ☐ Where do you shop for clothing?
☐ ☐ Why do you shop there?

Ask Answer
☐ ☐ In your opinion, what's the best place to buy a TV or other home entertainment product?
☐ ☐ Why do you think so?

38 Ⓐ Ⓑ Ⓒ Ⓓ   **39** Ⓐ Ⓑ Ⓒ Ⓓ   **40** Ⓐ Ⓑ Ⓒ Ⓓ

STOP

A SCHEDULES

 **Clinic**

Mon–Fri	8:30 – 7:30
Sat	8:30 – 5:30
Sun	Closed

Post Office

Mon–Fri	8:00 – 5:00
Sat	8:00 – 1:00
Sun	Closed

Motor Vehicles Department

Open

M–Th	8:30 – 4:30
Fri	8:30 – 7:00
Sat	9:00 – 12:00
Closed Sunday	

Library

Hours

M, W, F	8:30 AM – 9:00 PM
T, Th	9:00 AM – 6:00 PM
Sat, Sun	11:00 AM – 7:00 PM

UNITED STATES POSTAL SERVICE **COLLECTION TIMES**

Monday – Friday	Saturday	Sunday
9:00 AM 2:00 PM 11:30 AM	1:00 PM	Holiday

Location of Express Mail Drop:	For information call:
250 Adams Street	(800) ASK-USPS

Look at the schedules. Choose the correct answer.

Example:

What time does the clinic open on Saturday?

- Ⓐ At 5:30.
- Ⓑ At 7:30.
- ⬤ At 8:30.
- Ⓓ It's closed.

1. What time does the clinic close on Wednesday?

- Ⓐ At 5:30.
- Ⓑ At 7:30.
- Ⓒ At 8:30.
- Ⓓ It's closed.

2. What time does the post office open on Tuesday?

- Ⓐ At 8:00.
- Ⓑ At 1:00.
- Ⓒ At 3:00.
- Ⓓ At 5:00.

3. How many hours is the Motor Vehicles Department open on Monday?

- Ⓐ Three.
- Ⓑ Eight.
- Ⓒ Nine.
- Ⓓ Ten.

4. What time does the library close on Thursday?

- Ⓐ At 6:00 AM.
- Ⓑ At 9:00 AM.
- Ⓒ At 6:00 PM.
- Ⓓ At 9:00 PM.

5. On which day is the Motor Vehicles Department open later in the evening?

- Ⓐ Saturday.
- Ⓑ Monday.
- Ⓒ Thursday.
- Ⓓ Friday.

6. What time do they pick up the mail on weekday afternoons?

- Ⓐ At 2:00 PM.
- Ⓑ At 1:00 PM.
- Ⓒ At 11:30 AM.
- Ⓓ At 9:00 AM.

7. How many times do they pick up the mail on weekday mornings?

- Ⓐ One.
- Ⓑ Two.
- Ⓒ Three.
- Ⓓ Four.

1 Ⓐ Ⓑ Ⓒ Ⓓ   3 Ⓐ Ⓑ Ⓒ Ⓓ   5 Ⓐ Ⓑ Ⓒ Ⓓ   7 Ⓐ Ⓑ Ⓒ Ⓓ

2 Ⓐ Ⓑ Ⓒ Ⓓ   4 Ⓐ Ⓑ Ⓒ Ⓓ   6 Ⓐ Ⓑ Ⓒ Ⓓ

Go to the next page ⟩

Look at the map. Choose the correct place.

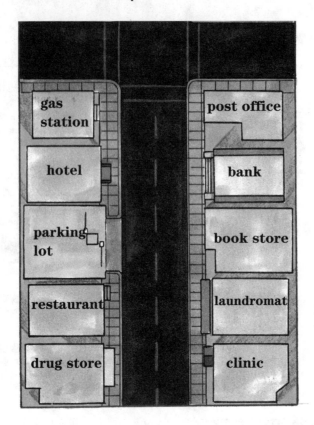

Example:

It's across from the hotel.

- Ⓐ The gas station.
- Ⓑ The bank.
- Ⓒ The parking lot.
- Ⓓ The post office.   Ⓐ ● Ⓒ Ⓓ

8. It's next to the clinic.
   - Ⓐ The drug store.
   - Ⓑ The book store.
   - Ⓒ The laundromat.
   - Ⓓ The restaurant.

9. It's on the east side of the street, between the bank and the laundromat.
   - Ⓐ The post office.
   - Ⓑ The parking lot.
   - Ⓒ The hotel.
   - Ⓓ The book store.

10. It's on the west side of the street, north of the hotel.
    - Ⓐ The parking lot.
    - Ⓑ The gas station.
    - Ⓒ The bank.
    - Ⓓ The post office.

11. It's on the east side of the street, south of the laundromat.
    - Ⓐ The clinic.
    - Ⓑ The restaurant.
    - Ⓒ The drug store.
    - Ⓓ The book store.

8 Ⓐ Ⓑ Ⓒ Ⓓ   9 Ⓐ Ⓑ Ⓒ Ⓓ   10 Ⓐ Ⓑ Ⓒ Ⓓ   11 Ⓐ Ⓑ Ⓒ Ⓓ

Go to the next page ⟩

C READING: A Bus Schedule

Look at the bus schedule.
Choose the correct answer.

Example:

Where does this bus route start?
- (A) Russell Avenue.
- (B) Metro Plaza.
- (C) Custis Drive.
- (D) King Street. (A) (B) (C) ●

12. Where does this bus route end?
- (A) King Street.
- (B) Braddock Road.
- (C) Russell Avenue.
- (D) Metro Plaza.

13. What time does the first bus leave King Street?
- (A) 5:40 AM.
- (B) 6:13 AM.
- (C) 6:50 PM.
- (D) 7:23 PM.

14. What time does the last bus arrive at Custis Drive?
- (A) 6:06 AM.
- (B) 6:13 AM.
- (C) 7:16 PM.
- (D) 7:23 PM.

15. When does the 7:00 AM bus arrive at Russell Avenue?
- (A) 7:00 AM.
- (B) 7:11 AM.
- (C) 7:11 PM.
- (D) 7:21 AM.

16. Which bus doesn't stop at Metro Plaza?
- (A) The 6:00 AM bus from King Street.
- (B) The 9:00 AM bus from King Street.
- (C) The 1:05 PM bus from King Street.
- (D) The 3:05 PM bus from King Street.

Route 18A

King Street	Braddock Road	Russell Avenue	Custis Drive	Metro Plaza
Weekdays				
5:40 AM	5:51	6:01	6:06	6:13
6:00	6:11	6:21	6:26	6:33
6:20	6:31	6:41	6:46	6:53
6:40	6:51	7:01	7:06	7:13
7:00	7:11	7:21	7:26	7:33
7:20	7:31	7:41	7:46	7:53
7:40	7:51	8:01	8:06	8:13
8:00	8:11	8:21	8:26	8:33
8:20	8:31	8:41	8:46	8:53
8:40	8:51	9:01	9:06	9:13
9:00	9:11	9:21	9:26	9:33
10:05	10:15	10:25	10:30	-
11:05	11:15	11:25	11:30	-
12:05 PM	12:15	12:25	12:30	-
1:05	1:15	1:25	1:30	-
2:05	2:15	2:25	2:30	-
3:05	3:16	3:26	3:31	3:38
3:50	4:01	4:11	4:16	4:23
4:10	4:21	4:31	4:36	4:43
4:30	4:41	4:51	4:56	5:03
4:50	5:01	5:11	5:16	5:23
5:10	5:21	5:31	5:36	5:43
5:30	5:41	5:51	5:56	6:03
5:50	6:01	6:11	6:16	6:23
6:10	6:21	6:31	6:36	6:43
6:30	6:41	6:51	6:56	7:03
6:50	7:01	7:11	7:16	7:23

17. How long does it take any bus to go from King Street to Metro Plaza?
- (A) 11 minutes.
- (B) 12 minutes.
- (C) 30 minutes.
- (D) 33 minutes.

18. It's 12:30 PM, and you're at the bus stop on King Street. How long do you have to wait for the bus?
- (A) 1 hour.
- (B) 35 minutes.
- (C) 30 minutes.
- (D) 5 minutes.

....

12 (A) (B) (C) (D)   14 (A) (B) (C) (D)   16 (A) (B) (C) (D)   18 (A) (B) (C) (D)

13 (A) (B) (C) (D)   15 (A) (B) (C) (D)   17 (A) (B) (C) (D)

Go to the next page ⟩

Choose the correct sign.

A

B

C

D

Example:

There are train tracks ahead.
Watch out for trains.

Ⓐ Ⓑ ● Ⓓ

19. No left turn.

Ⓐ Ⓑ Ⓒ Ⓓ

20. There's a crosswalk ahead.
Watch out for pedestrians.

Ⓐ Ⓑ Ⓒ Ⓓ

21. When you enter this road, let the other
cars already on the road go first.

Ⓐ Ⓑ Ⓒ Ⓓ

Choose the correct sign.

A

B

C

D

Example:

"Stop! You can't enter this street from
here!"

Ⓐ Ⓑ Ⓒ ●

22. "Slow down! You're in a school zone!"

Ⓐ Ⓑ Ⓒ Ⓓ

23. "You can't make a U-turn here!"

Ⓐ Ⓑ Ⓒ Ⓓ

24. "Turn around! You're going in the wrong
direction!"

Ⓐ Ⓑ Ⓒ Ⓓ

....

19 Ⓐ Ⓑ Ⓒ Ⓓ   21 Ⓐ Ⓑ Ⓒ Ⓓ   23 Ⓐ Ⓑ Ⓒ Ⓓ

20 Ⓐ Ⓑ Ⓒ Ⓓ   22 Ⓐ Ⓑ Ⓒ Ⓓ   24 Ⓐ Ⓑ Ⓒ Ⓓ

Go to the next page ➔

Example:

I want to send this _____ to Texas.
- (A) postcard
- ● package
- (C) letter
- (D) envelope

25. Do you want to send it _____ surface mail or air mail?
- (A) for
- (B) with
- (C) by
- (D) from

26. _____ recommend?
- (A) What does it
- (B) What do I
- (C) What does he
- (D) What do you

27. Let's see. It weighs eight _____ and eleven ounces.
- (A) inches
- (B) pounds
- (C) feet
- (D) miles

28. How much will it _____?
- (A) cost
- (B) costs
- (C) send
- (D) sends

29. _____ $4.50 surface mail or $7.25 air mail.
- (A) I'll cost
- (B) You'll cost
- (C) It'll cost
- (D) They'll cost

30. _____ will it take to get there by surface mail?
- (A) How much
- (B) How many
- (C) How short
- (D) How long

31. About ten _____.
- (A) miles
- (B) ounces
- (C) days
- (D) feet

All right.

32. I think I'll send it by surface mail. And I'd also like a book of first-class _____, please.
- (A) postcards
- (B) stamps
- (C) money orders
- (D) aerogrammes

....

25 (A) (B) (C) (D)   28 (A) (B) (C) (D)   31 (A) (B) (C) (D)

26 (A) (B) (C) (D)   29 (A) (B) (C) (D)   32 (A) (B) (C) (D)

27 (A) (B) (C) (D)   30 (A) (B) (C) (D)

Go to the next page

G CLOZE READING: Simple Written Directions

Choose the correct answers to complete the directions.

Here are directions from our school to my apartment. Walk west along School Street

for Ⓐ to ● next Ⓒ Pond Road and drive Ⓐ for Ⓑ turn Ⓒ ³³ right. Walk north on Pond Road three

blocks Ⓐ walks Ⓑ turns Ⓒ ³⁴ to River Street and turn left. Walk west on River Street and you'll

see my apartment building in Ⓐ on Ⓑ with Ⓒ ³⁵ the right, across Ⓐ around Ⓑ between Ⓒ ³⁶ a bank

and a bakery.

H LISTENING ASSESSMENT: Compass Directions

Read and listen to the questions. Then listen to the conversation and answer the questions.

37. In which direction is the post office?
- Ⓐ North.
- Ⓑ South.
- Ⓒ East.
- Ⓓ West.

38. In which direction is the library?
- Ⓐ North.
- Ⓑ South.
- Ⓒ East.
- Ⓓ West.

39. In which direction is the shopping mall?
- Ⓐ North.
- Ⓑ South.
- Ⓒ East.
- Ⓓ West.

40. In which direction is the zoo?
- Ⓐ North.
- Ⓑ South.
- Ⓒ East.
- Ⓓ West.

I WRITING ASSESSMENT

Draw a map and write simple directions from your school to your home. (Use a separate sheet of paper.)

J SPEAKING ASSESSMENT

I can ask and answer these questions:

Ask Answer
- ☐ ☐ Can you tell me how to get to the post office?
- ☐ ☐ Could you please tell me how to get to the airport from here?
- ☐ ☐ Would you please tell me how to get to the nearest hospital?
- ☐ ☐ What's the best way to get to your home from here?

---

33 Ⓐ Ⓑ Ⓒ Ⓓ   35 Ⓐ Ⓑ Ⓒ Ⓓ   37 Ⓐ Ⓑ Ⓒ Ⓓ   39 Ⓐ Ⓑ Ⓒ Ⓓ

34 Ⓐ Ⓑ Ⓒ Ⓓ   36 Ⓐ Ⓑ Ⓒ Ⓓ   38 Ⓐ Ⓑ Ⓒ Ⓓ   40 Ⓐ Ⓑ Ⓒ Ⓓ

Name _____

Date _____ Class _____

A HELP WANTED ADS

Look at the Help Wanted ads. Choose the correct answer.

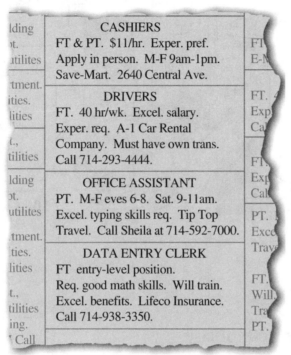

CASHIERS
FT & PT. $11/hr. Exper. pref.
Apply in person. M-F 9am-1pm.
Save-Mart. 2640 Central Ave.

DRIVERS
FT. 40 hr/wk. Excel. salary.
Exper. req. A-1 Car Rental
Company. Must have own trans.
Call 714-293-4444.

OFFICE ASSISTANT
PT. M-F eves 6-8. Sat. 9-11am.
Excel. typing skills req. Tip Top
Travel. Call Sheila at 714-592-7000.

DATA ENTRY CLERK
FT entry-level position.
Req. good math skills. Will train.
Excel. benefits. Lifeco Insurance.
Call 714-938-3350.

Example:

Which company only has a part-time job available?

Ⓐ Save-Mart.
Ⓑ A-1 Car Rental Company.
Ⓒ Lifeco Insurance.
Ⓓ Tip Top Travel.   Ⓐ Ⓑ Ⓒ ⬤

1. Which ad gives information about the salary?

   Ⓐ The ad for drivers.
   Ⓑ The ad for an office assistant.
   Ⓒ The ad for cashiers.
   Ⓓ The ad for a data entry clerk.

2. Victor wants to apply for a job as a driver. What does he have to do?

   Ⓐ He has to call Save-Mart.
   Ⓑ He has to call 714-938-3350.
   Ⓒ He has to call 714-592-7000.
   Ⓓ He has to call 714-293-4444.

3. How many hours per week does the office assistant work?

   Ⓐ 10 hours per week.
   Ⓑ 12 hours per week.
   Ⓒ 14 hours per week.
   Ⓓ 40 hours per week.

4. What does a person need for the job at Lifeco Insurance?

   Ⓐ Math skills.
   Ⓑ Excellent typing skills.
   Ⓒ Experience as a cashier.
   Ⓓ Transportation.

5. Which sentence ISN'T true about the jobs at Save-Mart?

   Ⓐ Experience is preferred.
   Ⓑ A person doesn't have to call first to apply for a job.
   Ⓒ Experience is required.
   Ⓓ There are part-time and full-time jobs available.

1 Ⓐ Ⓑ Ⓒ Ⓓ   3 Ⓐ Ⓑ Ⓒ Ⓓ   5 Ⓐ Ⓑ Ⓒ Ⓓ

2 Ⓐ Ⓑ Ⓒ Ⓓ   4 Ⓐ Ⓑ Ⓒ Ⓓ

Go to the next page ▷

B GRAMMAR IN CONTEXT: Job Interview Questions About Skills & Work History

Example:

Tell me about _____ skills.

- (A) my
- ● your
- (C) its
- (D) their

6. I _____ use a cash register, and I _____ how to take inventory.

- (A) know . . . can
- (B) know . . . know
- (C) can . . . can
- (D) can . . . know

7. Do you have any _____ as a cashier?

- (A) work
- (B) work experience
- (C) help wanted
- (D) experience preferred

8. Yes. I _____ a cashier in my last job.

- (A) work
- (B) worked
- (C) was
- (D) am

9. Where _____ work and for how long?

- (A) you did
- (B) did you
- (C) you were
- (D) were you

10. I worked at the Save-Rite Market _____ two years.

- (A) for
- (B) from
- (C) during
- (D) in

C DESCRIBING A WORK SCHEDULE

Look at Maria Perdomo's work schedule. Choose the correct answer.

WORK SCHEDULE			SEPTEMBER				
	SUN	MON	TUE	WED	THU	FRI	SAT
Start	12:00 PM	8:30 AM	8:30 AM		9:15 AM	9:15 AM	7:45 AM
End	9:00 PM	2:30 PM	2:30 PM		6:15 PM	6:15 PM	4:45 PM

Ex: How many days does she work this week?

- (A) Four.
- (B) Five.
- ● Six.
- (D) Seven.

11. Which day is her day off?

- (A) Monday.
- (B) Wednesday.
- (C) Saturday.
- (D) Sunday.

12. What time does she begin work on Thursday?

- (A) 9:15 AM.
- (B) 6:15 PM.
- (C) 8:30 AM.
- (D) 12:00 PM.

13. What time does she finish work on Tuesday?

- (A) 8:30 AM.
- (B) 6:15 PM.
- (C) 4:45 PM.
- (D) 2:30 PM.

14. How many hours does she work on Friday?

- (A) Six.
- (B) Eight.
- (C) Nine.
- (D) Ten.

15. What is the total number of hours she works this week?

- (A) 35.
- (B) 40.
- (C) 48.
- (D) 50.

. . . .

6 (A) (B) (C) (D)   9 (A) (B) (C) (D)   12 (A) (B) (C) (D)   15 (A) (B) (C) (D)

7 (A) (B) (C) (D)   10 (A) (B) (C) (D)   13 (A) (B) (C) (D)

8 (A) (B) (C) (D)   11 (A) (B) (C) (D)   14 (A) (B) (C) (D)

Go to the next page ▷

Ex: Hello, Ms. Pratt. This is Ted Simon. I'm afraid I _____ come to work today.
- ● can't
- Ⓑ can
- Ⓒ have
- Ⓓ can to

17. _____ feel very sick.
- Ⓐ I
- Ⓑ I'm
- Ⓒ You
- Ⓓ You're

16. What's the _____, Ted?
- Ⓐ with you
- Ⓑ sick
- Ⓒ why
- Ⓓ matter

18. Okay. _____ come to work today.
- Ⓐ Don't have to
- Ⓑ You don't have to
- Ⓒ I have to
- Ⓓ I don't have to

19. Ms. Pratt? This is Debbie Simpson. _____ be late for work this morning.
- Ⓐ I'll arrive
- Ⓑ I'm going to arrive
- Ⓒ I'm going to
- Ⓓ I'm going

What happened?

20. My bus _____ a flat tire. I _____ wait for another bus.
- Ⓐ has . . . have to
- Ⓑ have . . . has to
- Ⓒ has . . . has to
- Ⓓ have . . . have to

Don't worry about it, Debbie. I'll see you when you get here.

Excuse me, Mr. Hunter. Can I possibly change my work schedule for next week?

21. What _____ change?
- Ⓐ you want
- Ⓑ do you want
- Ⓒ you want to
- Ⓓ do you want to

22. I'd like to change my _____ to Tuesday. I have to take my children to the doctor that day.
- Ⓐ off day
- Ⓑ day off
- Ⓒ sick day
- Ⓓ weekend day

23. I understand. Yes, you have my _____.
- Ⓐ application
- Ⓑ schedule
- Ⓒ permission
- Ⓓ change

16 Ⓐ Ⓑ Ⓒ Ⓓ   18 Ⓐ Ⓑ Ⓒ Ⓓ   20 Ⓐ Ⓑ Ⓒ Ⓓ   22 Ⓐ Ⓑ Ⓒ Ⓓ

17 Ⓐ Ⓑ Ⓒ Ⓓ   19 Ⓐ Ⓑ Ⓒ Ⓓ   21 Ⓐ Ⓑ Ⓒ Ⓓ   23 Ⓐ Ⓑ Ⓒ Ⓓ

Go to the next page ⟩

━━━ ACCIDENT REPORT ━━━

1. Name of Employee / Injured Person	2. Job Title

3. Sex	4. Date of Birth	5. SSN

6. Day, Date, & Time of Occurrence	7. Location of Accident

8. Description of Injury (Part of body injured & nature of injury)

9. What was the accident and how did it occur?

10. Safety Equipment or Procedures Being Used at Time of Accident

11. Contributing Factors (e.g., lack of training)

12. What do you recommend to prevent this accident in the future?

13. Name & Position of Witness(es)	14. Name of Physician	15. Employee's Signature

Look at the information. Choose the correct line on the form.

24. Shipping department
- Ⓐ Line 2
- Ⓑ Line 6
- Ⓒ Line 7
- Ⓓ Line 8

25. Friday, 2/10/08, 4:15 PM
- Ⓐ Line 3
- Ⓑ Line 4
- Ⓒ Line 5
- Ⓓ Line 6

26. I broke my right foot.
- Ⓐ Line 7
- Ⓑ Line 8
- Ⓒ Line 9
- Ⓓ Line 11

27. A big box fell off the forklift and dropped on my foot.
- Ⓐ Line 7
- Ⓑ Line 8
- Ⓒ Line 9
- Ⓓ Line 10

28. Michael Fuentes, stock clerk
- Ⓐ Line 1
- Ⓑ Line 2
- Ⓒ Line 10
- Ⓓ Line 13

29. The company should buy stronger protective shoes for employees in the shipping department.
- Ⓐ Line 12
- Ⓑ Line 11
- Ⓒ Line 10
- Ⓓ Line 9

....

24 Ⓐ Ⓑ Ⓒ Ⓓ   26 Ⓐ Ⓑ Ⓒ Ⓓ   28 Ⓐ Ⓑ Ⓒ Ⓓ

25 Ⓐ Ⓑ Ⓒ Ⓓ   27 Ⓐ Ⓑ Ⓒ Ⓓ   29 Ⓐ Ⓑ Ⓒ Ⓓ

Go to the next page ⟩

F READING: A Paycheck Stub

```
APRIL COMPANY                    RIZAL, J.                  EMP. NO. 60159
================================================================
PAY PERIOD ENDING        RATE          HOURS              EARNINGS
     120508              9.97            40                 398.80
================================================================
FED TAX      33.59                    EARNINGS             398.80
FICA/MED     26.47                    TAXES                 70.92
STATE TAX    10.86                    DEDUCTIONS            43.16
HEALTH       43.16
                                      NET PAY              284.72
- - - - - - - - - - - - - - - - - - - - - - - - - - - - - - - - -
APRIL COMPANY                              CHECK NO. 16889
                                          DATE ISSUED 121808

Pay to      JOSE RIZAL                         $284.72
TWO HUNDRED EIGHTY-FOUR DOLLARS AND SEVENTY-TWO CENTS
                                              Dee Boss
```

Look at the paycheck stub. Choose the correct answer.

30. What is Mr. Rizal's salary?
- Ⓐ 40 hours a week.
- Ⓑ $9.97 per hour.
- Ⓒ $284.72 per year.
- Ⓓ $398.80 per year.

31. How much did he earn during this pay period?
- Ⓐ $398.80.
- Ⓑ $9.97.
- Ⓒ $40.00.
- Ⓓ $284.72.

32. How much was the deduction for state taxes?
- Ⓐ $43.16.
- Ⓑ $33.59.
- Ⓒ $26.47.
- Ⓓ $10.86.

33. How much pay did Mr. Rizal take home after deductions?
- Ⓐ $398.80.
- Ⓑ $284.72.
- Ⓒ $40 per hour.
- Ⓓ $9.97 per hour.

G CLOZE READING: Nonverbal Behavior at the Job Interview

Choose the correct answers to complete the story.

The information you give at a job interview is important, but your nonverbal behavior is also important. You should dress [neat (A) | neatly (●) | sloppily (C)]. Shake hands [to (A) | with (B) | for (C)] [34] the interviewer firmly. A firm handshake shows that you are [friend (A) | friends (B) | friendly (C)] [35] and confident. Make "eye contact." Look at the interviewer [direct (A) | directly (B) | director (C)] [36]. Don't speak too quickly, and don't speak too loudly or too [softly (A) | softer (B) | soft (C)] [37]. And don't forget to smile!

. . . .

30 Ⓐ Ⓑ Ⓒ Ⓓ   **32** Ⓐ Ⓑ Ⓒ Ⓓ   **35** Ⓐ Ⓑ Ⓒ Ⓓ

31 Ⓐ Ⓑ Ⓒ Ⓓ   **33** Ⓐ Ⓑ Ⓒ Ⓓ   **36** Ⓐ Ⓑ Ⓒ Ⓓ

34 Ⓐ Ⓑ Ⓒ Ⓓ   **37** Ⓐ Ⓑ Ⓒ Ⓓ

```
                                                Go to the next page ⟩
```

Read and listen to the questions. Then listen to the conversation and answer the questions.

38. What kind of position is the person applying for?
    - Ⓐ A job as a cashier.
    - Ⓑ An office position.
    - Ⓒ A position in a supermarket.
    - Ⓓ A job in a computer factory.

39. Where is the conversation taking place?
    - Ⓐ At the Larsen Real Estate Agency.
    - Ⓑ At the Citywide Supermarket.
    - Ⓒ At Landmark Data Management.
    - Ⓓ At the Johnson Insurance Company.

40. How many years of work experience does the applicant have?
    - Ⓐ 1 year.
    - Ⓑ 2 years.
    - Ⓒ 3 years.
    - Ⓓ 6 years.

I WRITING: Complete the Job Application Form

APPLICATION FOR EMPLOYMENT

Name _____ Social Security Number_____

Address _____
       Street   City   State   ZIP Code

Phone No. ( ) _____ Age (if under 21) _____ Birth Date (if under 21) ___/___/___
                                                                              Month Day Year

Position Desired _____ Salary Desired _____ Date you can start _____

EDUCATION

Type of School	Name	Location	Years Completed	Graduated?
High School				
College				
Other				

EMPLOYMENT (Start with present or most recent employer)

Date (Month/Year)	Name and Address of Employer	Position	Salary
From To			
From To			
From To			

Date _____ Signature _____

J SPEAKING ASSESSMENT

I can ask and answer these questions:

Ask Answer
- ☐ ☐ What kind of job are you looking for?
- ☐ ☐ Tell me about your skills and abilities.
- ☐ ☐ Tell me about your previous education.
- ☐ ☐ Tell me a little about yourself.

Ask Answer
- ☐ ☐ Are you currently employed?
- ☐ ☐ Tell me about your work history.
- ☐ ☐ Why do you want to work here?
- ☐ ☐ Do you have any questions about the position?

38 Ⓐ Ⓑ Ⓒ Ⓓ   39 Ⓐ Ⓑ Ⓒ Ⓓ   40 Ⓐ Ⓑ Ⓒ Ⓓ

STOP

Name _____

Date _____ Class _____

9

Choose the correct answer.

1. He took _____ for his headache.
   - (A) a cotton ball
   - (B) aspirin
   - (C) a band-aid
   - (D) adhesive tape

2. I cut my finger. Could you please get _____ from the first-aid kit?
   - (A) a band-aid
   - (B) a piece of paper
   - (C) a cotton ball
   - (D) an ACE bandage

3. You should put some _____ on that cut.
   - (A) ice cream
   - (B) toothpaste
   - (C) aspirin
   - (D) antibiotic ointment

4. I'm going to clean the wound with _____.
   - (A) adhesive tape
   - (B) a napkin
   - (C) an antiseptic cleansing wipe
   - (D) a band-aid

5. The doctor used _____ to take the splinter out of my finger.
   - (A) a knife
   - (B) a screwdriver
   - (C) scissors
   - (D) tweezers

6. The school nurse wrapped my ankle with _____.
   - (A) an ACE bandage
   - (B) adhesive tape
   - (C) toilet paper
   - (D) an antiseptic cleansing wipe

7. You scraped your knee. I'm going to put on _____.
   - (A) adhesive tape
   - (B) a sterile gauze dressing pad
   - (C) a cotton ball
   - (D) an ACE bandage

8. Attach the gauze pad with _____.
   - (A) adhesive tape
   - (B) an ACE bandage
   - (C) a string
   - (D) a band-aid

1 (A) (B) (C) (D)   3 (A) (B) (C) (D)   5 (A) (B) (C) (D)   7 (A) (B) (C) (D)

2 (A) (B) (C) (D)   4 (A) (B) (C) (D)   6 (A) (B) (C) (D)   8 (A) (B) (C) (D)

© 2008 Pearson Education, Inc.
Duplication for classroom use is permitted.

Go to the next page

B GRAMMAR IN CONTEXT: Calling 911

Choose the correct answer to complete the conversations.

Emergency Operator.

9. I want to _____ a robbery!
- Ⓐ do
- Ⓑ catch
- Ⓒ report
- Ⓓ make

10. _____ the address?
- Ⓐ When is
- Ⓑ Who is
- Ⓒ How is
- Ⓓ What is

241 Central Avenue, Apartment 5.

11. And please tell me _____.
- Ⓐ who happened
- Ⓑ when it's happening
- Ⓒ what happened
- Ⓓ what's going to happen

12. Burglars broke into our apartment while we _____
- Ⓐ working
- Ⓑ were working
- Ⓒ work
- Ⓓ works

13. Okay. We'll send a patrol car _____.
- Ⓐ right away
- Ⓑ yesterday
- Ⓒ next month
- Ⓓ every day

Thank you.

This is the Fairfax Emergency Center. You're on a recorded line.

14. We need _____ at 650 Main Street!
- Ⓐ an emergency
- Ⓑ a prescription
- Ⓒ a first-aid kit
- Ⓓ an ambulance

What's the emergency?

15. I think my father is having _____.
- Ⓐ a very bad cold
- Ⓑ an upset stomach
- Ⓒ a heart attack
- Ⓓ an earache

An emergency vehicle is on the way.

Thank you.

9 Ⓐ Ⓑ Ⓒ Ⓓ   11 Ⓐ Ⓑ Ⓒ Ⓓ   13 Ⓐ Ⓑ Ⓒ Ⓓ   15 Ⓐ Ⓑ Ⓒ Ⓓ

10 Ⓐ Ⓑ Ⓒ Ⓓ   12 Ⓐ Ⓑ Ⓒ Ⓓ   14 Ⓐ Ⓑ Ⓒ Ⓓ

Go to the next page

16. Can you describe his _____?
- Ⓐ width
- Ⓑ height
- Ⓒ length
- Ⓓ weight

17. He was about six feet _____.
- Ⓐ long
- Ⓑ high
- Ⓒ tall
- Ⓓ height

18. What was his _____?
- Ⓐ with
- Ⓑ width
- Ⓒ wait
- Ⓓ weight

19. He weighed about 160 _____.
- Ⓐ pounds
- Ⓑ feet
- Ⓒ inches
- Ⓓ yards

20. What _____ was his hair?
- Ⓐ length
- Ⓑ color
- Ⓒ look
- Ⓓ weight

21. It was dark _____.
- Ⓐ thin
- Ⓑ short
- Ⓒ long
- Ⓓ brown

22. Can you describe his _____?
- Ⓐ wear
- Ⓑ wearing
- Ⓒ clothing
- Ⓓ wore

23. He was wearing a red _____ and a pair of gray _____.
- Ⓐ pants . . . shoes
- Ⓑ pants . . . shirt
- Ⓒ shirt . . . pants
- Ⓓ shoes . . . socks

D **READING: Warning Labels on Household Products**

Choose the correct warning label for each instruction.

Do not use with other household chemicals.	Avoid direct contact. Wear rubber gloves.	Harmful if swallowed.	Avoid prolonged breathing of vapors.
A	**B**	**C**	**D**

24. Do not eat or drink.
Ⓐ   Ⓑ   Ⓒ   Ⓓ

26. Use only in well-ventilated areas. Avoid fumes.
Ⓐ   Ⓑ   Ⓒ   Ⓓ

25. Do not get on skin.
Ⓐ   Ⓑ   Ⓒ   Ⓓ

27. Do not mix together with other products.
Ⓐ   Ⓑ   Ⓒ   Ⓓ

. . . .

16 Ⓐ Ⓑ Ⓒ Ⓓ   19 Ⓐ Ⓑ Ⓒ Ⓓ   22 Ⓐ Ⓑ Ⓒ Ⓓ   25 Ⓐ Ⓑ Ⓒ Ⓓ

17 Ⓐ Ⓑ Ⓒ Ⓓ   20 Ⓐ Ⓑ Ⓒ Ⓓ   23 Ⓐ Ⓑ Ⓒ Ⓓ   26 Ⓐ Ⓑ Ⓒ Ⓓ

18 Ⓐ Ⓑ Ⓒ Ⓓ   21 Ⓐ Ⓑ Ⓒ Ⓓ   24 Ⓐ Ⓑ Ⓒ Ⓓ   27 Ⓐ Ⓑ Ⓒ Ⓓ

Go to the next page ⟩

E READING: First-Aid Procedures

Choose the correct medical procedure for each emergency.

A	B	C	D
Cover the area with a cool wet cloth or put in cool water.	Try to remove stinger. Clean wound and apply cold cloth. Get medical help if there is itching, swelling, or if the person is dizzy, nauseous, or can't breathe.	Apply direct pressure with a clean cloth or sterile dressing directly on the wound.	If the victim cannot speak, breathe, or cough, ask for someone to call 911 and then perform the Heimlich maneuver.

28. bleeding
    Ⓐ Ⓑ Ⓒ Ⓓ

29. choking
    Ⓐ Ⓑ Ⓒ Ⓓ

30. bee sting
    Ⓐ Ⓑ Ⓒ Ⓓ

31. minor burn
    Ⓐ Ⓑ Ⓒ Ⓓ

F LEARNING SKILL: Categorizing Words; Word Sets

Choose the correct answer.

32. Which word isn't a *color*?
    Ⓐ blue   Ⓒ white
    Ⓑ shirt   Ⓓ brown

33. Which word doesn't describe *weight*?
    Ⓐ heavy   Ⓒ light
    Ⓑ fat   Ⓓ short

34. Which word isn't a *form of transportation*?
    Ⓐ telephone   Ⓒ train
    Ⓑ airplane   Ⓓ bus

35. Which word isn't a *season*?
    Ⓐ spring   Ⓒ snowing
    Ⓑ summer   Ⓓ winter

36. Which word isn't a *month*?
    Ⓐ May   Ⓒ August
    Ⓑ Monday   Ⓓ June

37. Which word doesn't describe *height*?
    Ⓐ heavy   Ⓒ short
    Ⓑ tall   Ⓓ medium height

G LISTENING ASSESSMENT: An Emergency Call

Read and listen to the questions. Then listen to the conversation and answer the questions.

38. When did the person fall?
    Ⓐ While she was on a trip.
    Ⓑ While she was in her apartment.
    Ⓒ While she was on the phone.
    Ⓓ While she was walking down the stairs.

39. What's their address?
    Ⓐ 13 East Street.
    Ⓑ 13 West Street.
    Ⓒ 30 East Street.
    Ⓓ 30 West Street.

40. Where is their apartment?
    Ⓐ On the 5th floor.
    Ⓑ On the 6th floor.
    Ⓒ Apartment 6-C.
    Ⓓ Apartment 6-G.

H WRITING ASSESSMENT: Fill Out the Form

Name _____

Height _____ Weight _____

Hair Color _____ Eye Color _____

I SPEAKING ASSESSMENT

I can ask and answer these questions:

Ask Answer
☐ ☐ What's your height?
☐ ☐ What's your hair color?
☐ ☐ What color are your eyes?
☐ ☐ What are you wearing today?

---

28 Ⓐ Ⓑ Ⓒ Ⓓ   31 Ⓐ Ⓑ Ⓒ Ⓓ   35 Ⓐ Ⓑ Ⓒ Ⓓ   38 Ⓐ Ⓑ Ⓒ Ⓓ

29 Ⓐ Ⓑ Ⓒ Ⓓ   32 Ⓐ Ⓑ Ⓒ Ⓓ   36 Ⓐ Ⓑ Ⓒ Ⓓ   39 Ⓐ Ⓑ Ⓒ Ⓓ

30 Ⓐ Ⓑ Ⓒ Ⓓ   33 Ⓐ Ⓑ Ⓒ Ⓓ   37 Ⓐ Ⓑ Ⓒ Ⓓ   40 Ⓐ Ⓑ Ⓒ Ⓓ

34 Ⓐ Ⓑ Ⓒ Ⓓ

STOP

Name _____

Date _____ **Class** _____

10

A HOUSING ADS

Look at the classified ads for housing. Choose the correct answer.

2 BR 1 BA, d/w, $950 incl util. 273-4651.	3BR 2 BA, big apt, d/w, cac, w/d, $1400 + util. Avail 9/15. 727-4981.
1 BR 1 BA, w/w, catv, nr hospital, $750 + util. Avail 10/1. 589-7315.	2 BR 1 1/2 BA, pkg, nr airport, d/w, incl catv, $875 + elec. 863-4193.

1. You're looking for a one-bedroom apartment. Which number will you call?
   - Ⓐ 273-4651.
   - Ⓑ 589-7315.
   - Ⓒ 727-4981.
   - Ⓓ 863-4193.

2. You need an apartment with two bathrooms. Which number will you call?
   - Ⓐ 863-4193.
   - Ⓑ 273-4651.
   - Ⓒ 589-7315.
   - Ⓓ 727-4981.

3. Which apartment includes utilities?
   - Ⓐ The 2-bedroom apartment with 1 bath.
   - Ⓑ The 2-bedroom apartment with 1 1/2 baths.
   - Ⓒ The 3-bedroom apartment.
   - Ⓓ The 1-bedroom apartment.

4. Which apartment doesn't have a dishwasher?
   - Ⓐ The 2-bedroom apartment with 1 bath.
   - Ⓑ The 2-bedroom apartment with 1 1/2 baths.
   - Ⓒ The 1-bedroom apartment.
   - Ⓓ The 3-bedroom apartment.

5. Which apartment is available on Sept. 15?
   - Ⓐ The 2-bedroom apartment with 1 bath.
   - Ⓑ The 2-bedroom apartment with 1 1/2 baths.
   - Ⓒ The 1-bedroom apartment.
   - Ⓓ The 3-bedroom apartment.

6. How many of these apartments have cable TV?
   - Ⓐ One.
   - Ⓑ Two.
   - Ⓒ Three.
   - Ⓓ Four.

7. How much is the rent for the apartment near the hospital?
   - Ⓐ $750 plus utilities.
   - Ⓑ $875 plus electricity.
   - Ⓒ $950 plus utilities.
   - Ⓓ $1400 plus utilities.

8. What does the 3-bedroom apartment have that the other apartments don't have?
   - Ⓐ Two bathrooms and a dishwasher.
   - Ⓑ A dishwasher and central air conditioning.
   - Ⓒ A dishwasher and a washer and dryer.
   - Ⓓ A washer and dryer and central air conditioning.

9. You're a pilot. You and a friend are looking for an apartment. Which number will you call?
   - Ⓐ 863-4193.
   - Ⓑ 727-4981.
   - Ⓒ 273-4651.
   - Ⓓ 589-7315.

10. What does the 1-bedroom apartment have that the other apartments don't have?
   - Ⓐ Cable TV.
   - Ⓑ Wall-to-wall carpeting.
   - Ⓒ A dishwasher.
   - Ⓓ A washer and dryer.

Go to the next page ⟩

1 Ⓐ Ⓑ Ⓒ Ⓓ   3 Ⓐ Ⓑ Ⓒ Ⓓ   5 Ⓐ Ⓑ Ⓒ Ⓓ   7 Ⓐ Ⓑ Ⓒ Ⓓ   9 Ⓐ Ⓑ Ⓒ Ⓓ

2 Ⓐ Ⓑ Ⓒ Ⓓ   4 Ⓐ Ⓑ Ⓒ Ⓓ   6 Ⓐ Ⓑ Ⓒ Ⓓ   8 Ⓐ Ⓑ Ⓒ Ⓓ   10 Ⓐ Ⓑ Ⓒ Ⓓ

Choose the correct answer to complete the conversation.

11. Is the apartment furnished _____ unfurnished?
- Ⓐ and
- Ⓑ but
- Ⓒ or
- Ⓓ with

12. It's unfurnished. _____ any furniture in the unit.
- Ⓐ Isn't
- Ⓑ There isn't
- Ⓒ Aren't
- Ⓓ There aren't

13. Is there public _____ nearby?
- Ⓐ communication
- Ⓑ location
- Ⓒ station
- Ⓓ transportation

14. Yes. There's a bus stop _____ the corner.
- Ⓐ around
- Ⓑ between
- Ⓒ next
- Ⓓ across

15. _____ is the rent?
- Ⓐ How many
- Ⓑ What does it cost
- Ⓒ How much
- Ⓓ What is the price

16. _____
- Ⓐ On the third floor.
- Ⓑ On the first day of the month.
- Ⓒ Every month.
- Ⓓ $800 a month.

17. _____ a security deposit?
- Ⓐ Are you
- Ⓑ Is there
- Ⓒ Am I
- Ⓓ Is it

18. Yes. We require one month's rent in advance when you _____ the lease.
- Ⓐ sign
- Ⓑ print
- Ⓒ leave
- Ⓓ signature

19. Is the building in _____ neighborhood?
- Ⓐ a dangerous
- Ⓑ an empty
- Ⓒ an inconvenient
- Ⓓ a convenient

20. Yes. _____ many stores in the neighborhood, and _____ a school nearby.
- Ⓐ There is . . . there's
- Ⓑ There is . . . there are
- Ⓒ There are . . . there's
- Ⓓ There are . . . there are

21. Are pets _____?
- Ⓐ loud
- Ⓑ allowed
- Ⓒ may they
- Ⓓ can we

22. Yes. Dogs and cats _____.
- Ⓐ have permission
- Ⓑ is permitted
- Ⓒ are permitted
- Ⓓ are you allowed

11 Ⓐ Ⓑ Ⓒ Ⓓ   14 Ⓐ Ⓑ Ⓒ Ⓓ   17 Ⓐ Ⓑ Ⓒ Ⓓ   20 Ⓐ Ⓑ Ⓒ Ⓓ

12 Ⓐ Ⓑ Ⓒ Ⓓ   15 Ⓐ Ⓑ Ⓒ Ⓓ   18 Ⓐ Ⓑ Ⓒ Ⓓ   21 Ⓐ Ⓑ Ⓒ Ⓓ

13 Ⓐ Ⓑ Ⓒ Ⓓ   16 Ⓐ Ⓑ Ⓒ Ⓓ   19 Ⓐ Ⓑ Ⓒ Ⓓ   22 Ⓐ Ⓑ Ⓒ Ⓓ

Go to the next page →

23. Hello. This is David Lee, the new tenant in Apartment 412. There are _____ in my apartment.
- Ⓐ broken
- Ⓑ a problem
- Ⓒ many repairs
- Ⓓ many problems

24. What's the _____?
- Ⓐ matter
- Ⓑ repair
- Ⓒ problems
- Ⓓ troubles

25. The doorbell is broken. _____
- Ⓐ It doesn't open.
- Ⓑ It doesn't lock.
- Ⓒ It doesn't ring.
- Ⓓ It doesn't close.

26. _____ And what else?
- Ⓐ You see.
- Ⓑ I see.
- Ⓒ It sees.
- Ⓓ We see.

I understand.

27. The oven doesn't light. _____
- Ⓐ The kitchen is dark.
- Ⓑ I can't bake.
- Ⓒ I can't see inside the oven.
- Ⓓ My food always burns.

28. The bathtub is cracked. _____
- Ⓐ There's water on the bathroom floor.
- Ⓑ The roof is leaking.
- Ⓒ The sink is leaking.
- Ⓓ There's water on the kitchen floor.

29. Okay. _____
- Ⓐ Else?
- Ⓑ Other?
- Ⓒ Anything?
- Ⓓ Anything else?

30. Yes. One more thing. The kitchen sink is clogged. _____
- Ⓐ The water is too hot.
- Ⓑ The water is too cold.
- Ⓒ The water doesn't go down the drain.
- Ⓓ Water doesn't come out of the faucet.

31. All right. I'll send someone to _____ everything right away.
- Ⓐ repair
- Ⓑ break
- Ⓒ fixes
- Ⓓ will fix

Thank you very much.

32. You're welcome, and I _____ for the inconvenience.
- Ⓐ please
- Ⓑ thank you
- Ⓒ sorry
- Ⓓ apologize

23 Ⓐ Ⓑ Ⓒ Ⓓ   26 Ⓐ Ⓑ Ⓒ Ⓓ   29 Ⓐ Ⓑ Ⓒ Ⓓ   32 Ⓐ Ⓑ Ⓒ Ⓓ

24 Ⓐ Ⓑ Ⓒ Ⓓ   27 Ⓐ Ⓑ Ⓒ Ⓓ   30 Ⓐ Ⓑ Ⓒ Ⓓ

25 Ⓐ Ⓑ Ⓒ Ⓓ   28 Ⓐ Ⓑ Ⓒ Ⓓ   31 Ⓐ Ⓑ Ⓒ Ⓓ

Go to the next page ➤

D READING: A Floor Plan

Look at the floor plan for this apartment. Choose the correct answer.

33. How many bedrooms are there?
    - (A) One.
    - (B) Two.
    - (C) Three.
    - (D) Four.

34. How many closets are there?
    - (A) One.
    - (B) Two.
    - (C) Three.
    - (D) Four.

35. How many bathrooms are there?
    - (A) One.
    - (B) Two.
    - (C) Three.
    - (D) Four.

36. How many bathtubs are there?
    - (A) One.
    - (B) Two.
    - (C) Three.
    - (D) Four.

E LISTENING ASSESSMENT: Inquiring About a Rental Unit

Read and listen to the questions. Then listen to the conversation and answer the questions.

37. Where is the 1-bedroom apartment?
    - (A) On the first floor.
    - (B) On the second floor.
    - (C) On the fifth floor.
    - (D) On the sixth floor.

38. How much is the rent on the 2-bedroom unit?
    - (A) $800 a month.
    - (B) $800 a week.
    - (C) $1,100 a year.
    - (D) $1,100 a month.

39. Which pets are allowed in the building?
    - (A) Dogs, cats, and smaller pets.
    - (B) Cats and smaller pets.
    - (C) Cats only.
    - (D) Dogs only.

40. How much is the security deposit on the 1-bedroom apartment?
    - (A) $800
    - (B) $1,100
    - (C) $1,600
    - (D) $2,200

F WRITING ASSESSMENT

Describe your apartment or home. Write about the rooms, the building, and the neighborhood.
(Use a separate sheet of paper.)

G SPEAKING ASSESSMENT

I can ask and answer these questions:

Ask Answer

☐ ☐ How many rooms are there in your apartment or home? Describe them.

☐ ☐ What's your favorite room? Why?

☐ ☐ Tell me about your neighborhood.

33 (A) (B) (C) (D)   35 (A) (B) (C) (D)   37 (A) (B) (C) (D)   39 (A) (B) (C) (D)

34 (A) (B) (C) (D)   36 (A) (B) (C) (D)   38 (A) (B) (C) (D)   40 (A) (B) (C) (D)

STOP

Name _____

Date _____ Class _____

11

A IDENTIFYING PARTS OF THE FACE & BODY
Choose the correct answer.

Example:

(A) arm
(B) foot
● hand
(D) toe

1. (A) ears
   (B) fingers
   (C) toes
   (D) lips

2. (A) wrist
   (B) ankle
   (C) elbow
   (D) arm

3. (A) beard
   (B) mustache
   (C) eyebrow
   (D) eyelash

4. (A) wrist
   (B) shoulder
   (C) ankle
   (D) elbow

5. (A) hip
   (B) leg
   (C) shoulder
   (D) thigh

B COMMON SYMPTOMS
Choose the correct answer.

6. My temperature is 102° F. I have _____.
   (A) a sweater
   (B) an oven
   (C) high blood pressure
   (D) a fever

7. Timmy needs a tissue. He has _____.
   (A) a runny nose
   (B) a sore throat
   (C) a backache
   (D) a fever

8. Carla ate too much candy. Now she has _____.
   (A) an earache
   (B) a toothache
   (C) a cold
   (D) a runny nose

9. That music was loud! I have _____.
   (A) a stiff back
   (B) a cold
   (C) a head
   (D) an earache

10. I sang all day. Now I have _____.
    (A) a backache
    (B) an earache
    (C) a sore throat
    (D) a sprained ankle

11. I think I have a cold. I have a bad _____.
    (A) sneeze
    (B) cough
    (C) throat
    (D) nose

1 (A) (B) (C) (D)   4 (A) (B) (C) (D)   7 (A) (B) (C) (D)   10 (A) (B) (C) (D)

2 (A) (B) (C) (D)   5 (A) (B) (C) (D)   8 (A) (B) (C) (D)   11 (A) (B) (C) (D)

3 (A) (B) (C) (D)   6 (A) (B) (C) (D)   9 (A) (B) (C) (D)

Side by Side Plus Book 2
Unit 11 Achievement Test (Page 1 of 4)

© 2008 Pearson Education, Inc.
Duplication for classroom use is permitted.

Go to the next page

C GRAMMAR IN CONTEXT: Calling to Report an Absence; Making a Doctor Appointment

Choose the correct answer to complete the conversations.

Woodlawn Elementary School.

12. Hello. This is Amy Long. My son, Paul, _____ absent today because _____ sick.
- Ⓐ will . . . he's
- Ⓑ will be . . . he's
- Ⓒ won't be . . . he
- Ⓓ can't . . . he

13. _____ class is he in?
- Ⓐ Which
- Ⓑ Who
- Ⓒ Where
- Ⓓ When

He's in Mr. Wilson's 4th grade class.

Doctor's office.

14. Hello. This is Alicia Flores. I don't _____ well.
- Ⓐ sick   Ⓒ feel
- Ⓑ healthy   Ⓓ feeling

15. _____ the matter?
- Ⓐ How's
- Ⓑ Why's
- Ⓒ Where's
- Ⓓ What's

I have a very bad stomachache.

16. Do you want to make _____?
- Ⓐ medicine
- Ⓑ see the doctor
- Ⓒ a reservation
- Ⓓ an appointment

Yes, please.

17. _____ tomorrow at 2 PM?
- Ⓐ Can you come in
- Ⓑ Can you go
- Ⓒ Are you sick
- Ⓓ Is the doctor here

2 PM? Yes. Thank you.

D PROCEDURES DURING A MEDICAL EXAM

18. The nurse took my blood _____.
- Ⓐ pulse   Ⓒ pressure
- Ⓑ weight   Ⓓ temperature

20. He measured my _____ on the scale.
- Ⓐ wait   Ⓒ weight
- Ⓑ waist   Ⓓ pulse

19. The doctor listened to my heart with _____.
- Ⓐ a scale   Ⓒ an X-ray
- Ⓑ a stethoscope   Ⓓ a headphone

21. She _____ my eyes, ears, nose, and throat.
- Ⓐ took   Ⓒ measured
- Ⓑ listened to Ⓓ examined

....

12 Ⓐ Ⓑ Ⓒ Ⓓ 15 Ⓐ Ⓑ Ⓒ Ⓓ 18 Ⓐ Ⓑ Ⓒ Ⓓ 21 Ⓐ Ⓑ Ⓒ Ⓓ

13 Ⓐ Ⓑ Ⓒ Ⓓ 16 Ⓐ Ⓑ Ⓒ Ⓓ 19 Ⓐ Ⓑ Ⓒ Ⓓ

14 Ⓐ Ⓑ Ⓒ Ⓓ 17 Ⓐ Ⓑ Ⓒ Ⓓ 20 Ⓐ Ⓑ Ⓒ Ⓓ

Go to the next page ➤

22. The doctor recommended _____ for the rash on my arm.

- Ⓐ anti-itch cream
- Ⓑ throat lozenges
- Ⓒ cough syrup
- Ⓓ antacid tablets

23. I'm taking _____ for my upset stomach.

- Ⓐ cough syrup
- Ⓑ antacid tablets
- Ⓒ throat lozenges
- Ⓓ aspirin

24. The doctor gave me a prescription for _____ for my throat infection.

- Ⓐ vitamins
- Ⓑ cold medicine
- Ⓒ ear drops
- Ⓓ penicillin

25. I sneeze and cough every spring, so the clinic gives me a prescription for _____.

- Ⓐ throat lozenges
- Ⓑ cough syrup
- Ⓒ allergy medication
- Ⓓ cold medicine

F READING: Medicine Label Dosages

Choose the correct medicine label for each instruction.

CLR 4 tabs. 2x/day Rx	Lincoln Pharmacy 2 tsps. 2x/day Rx	Olympic Pharmacies Rx 2 caps. 2x/day	MacLeod Drugs 2 pills 4x/day
A	**B**	**C**	**D**

26. Take two pills four times a day.
Ⓐ Ⓑ Ⓒ Ⓓ

27. Take two teaspoons two times a day.
Ⓐ Ⓑ Ⓒ Ⓓ

28. Twice a day take four tablets.
Ⓐ Ⓑ Ⓒ Ⓓ

29. Take two capsules twice a day.
Ⓐ Ⓑ Ⓒ Ⓓ

G READING: Medicine Label Instructions

Brookdale Pharmacy Rx For external use only.	Park Pharmacy Take medication on an empty stomach. Rx	J&M Rx Avoid dairy products and chocolate while taking this medicine.	Sunrise Pharmacy Rx IMPORTANT. Finish all this medication
A	**B**	**C**	**D**

30. Do not drink milk or other milk products.
Ⓐ Ⓑ Ⓒ Ⓓ

31. Do not eat or drink this medicine.
Ⓐ Ⓑ Ⓒ Ⓓ

32. Take 1 hour before or 2–3 hours after you eat.
Ⓐ Ⓑ Ⓒ Ⓓ

33. Even if you feel better, don't stop taking this medicine.
Ⓐ Ⓑ Ⓒ Ⓓ

....

22 Ⓐ Ⓑ Ⓒ Ⓓ	25 Ⓐ Ⓑ Ⓒ Ⓓ	28 Ⓐ Ⓑ Ⓒ Ⓓ	31 Ⓐ Ⓑ Ⓒ Ⓓ
23 Ⓐ Ⓑ Ⓒ Ⓓ	26 Ⓐ Ⓑ Ⓒ Ⓓ	29 Ⓐ Ⓑ Ⓒ Ⓓ	32 Ⓐ Ⓑ Ⓒ Ⓓ
24 Ⓐ Ⓑ Ⓒ Ⓓ	27 Ⓐ Ⓑ Ⓒ Ⓓ	30 Ⓐ Ⓑ Ⓒ Ⓓ	33 Ⓐ Ⓑ Ⓒ Ⓓ

Go to the next page ⟩

H CLOZE READING: A Note to the Teacher

Deer Dare Dear Mr. Harper,
(A)   (B)   ●

My daughter, Jenny, was present absent not ³⁴ from school yesterday
                         (A)   (B)   (C)

reason because for ³⁵ she had a very full good bad ³⁶ stomachache and I took
(A)   (B)   (C)   (A)   (B)   (C)

her him it ³⁷ to the doctor.
(A) (B) (C)

Sincerely,

Barbara Taylor

I LISTENING ASSESSMENT: Making a Doctor Appointment

Read and listen to the questions. Then listen to the conversation and answer the questions.

38. When did she hurt her back?
    Ⓐ Today.
    Ⓑ Yesterday.
    Ⓒ Last Tuesday.
    Ⓓ Last Thursday.

39. Where did she hurt it?
    Ⓐ At home.
    Ⓑ At the clinic.
    Ⓒ On the telephone.
    Ⓓ On the job.

40. What time does she have to be at the clinic?
    Ⓐ 7:15 AM.
    Ⓑ 7:30 AM.
    Ⓒ 7:45 AM.
    Ⓓ 7:30 PM.

J WRITING ASSESSMENT: Fill Out the Medical History Form

MEDICAL HISTORY

Name _____ Date of Birth ____/____/____
     First   M. I.   Last   Month Day Year

Address _____ _____ _____ _____
        Number Street   City   State   Zip Code

Telephone: Home _____ Work _____ Height _____ Weight _____

Emergency Contact: Name _____ Relationship _____ Telephone _____

Do you have: YES NO   YES NO   YES NO
heart disease?   ☐   ☐   allergies?   ☐   ☐   other problems?   ☐   ☐
kidney disease?   ☐   ☐   headaches?   ☐   ☐   Do you smoke?   ☐   ☐
high blood pressure? ☐   ☐   trouble sleeping? ☐   ☐   Do you drink?   ☐   ☐
diabetes?   ☐   ☐   trouble eating? ☐   ☐   Are you taking medicine now? ☐ ☐

If you answered Yes above, explain: _____

K SPEAKING ASSESSMENT

I can ask and answer these questions:

Ask Answer
☐   ☐   How do you feel?
☐   ☐   When was your last appointment at
         a clinic or doctor's office?

Ask Answer
☐   ☐   Are you taking any medicine now?
☐   ☐   Is there any history of medical problems
         in your family? Explain.

34 Ⓐ Ⓑ Ⓒ Ⓓ   36 Ⓐ Ⓑ Ⓒ Ⓓ   38 Ⓐ Ⓑ Ⓒ Ⓓ   40 Ⓐ Ⓑ Ⓒ Ⓓ
35 Ⓐ Ⓑ Ⓒ Ⓓ   37 Ⓐ Ⓑ Ⓒ Ⓓ   39 Ⓐ Ⓑ Ⓒ Ⓓ

STOP

Name _____

Date _____ Class _____

A FAHRENHEIT & CELSIUS TEMPERATURES

Look at the thermometer. Choose the correct temperature.

1. 84° F.
   - Ⓐ 0° C.
   - Ⓑ 12° C.
   - Ⓒ 29° C.
   - Ⓓ 84° C.

2. 32° F.
   - Ⓐ −32° C.
   - Ⓑ 0° C.
   - Ⓒ 32° C.
   - Ⓓ 64° C.

3. −16° C.
   - Ⓐ 9° F.
   - Ⓑ 61° F.
   - Ⓒ −16° F.
   - Ⓓ −9° F.

4. 12° C.
   - Ⓐ −12° F.
   - Ⓑ 17° F.
   - Ⓒ 53° F.
   - Ⓓ 70° F.

B TEMPERATURE VALUES

Choose the correct temperature.

5. It's very hot today. It's _____.
   - Ⓐ 35° C.
   - Ⓑ 35° F.

6. It's very cold today. It's _____.
   - Ⓐ 28° C.
   - Ⓑ 15° F.

7. I have a fever. My temperature is _____.
   - Ⓐ 39° F.
   - Ⓑ 39° C.

8. The water is beginning to freeze. It's _____.
   - Ⓐ 0° C.
   - Ⓑ 0° F.

9. The cake is baking in the oven at _____.
   - Ⓐ 350° C.
   - Ⓑ 350° F.

10. The water is starting to boil. Its temperature is _____.
   - Ⓐ 100° C.
   - Ⓑ 100° F.

Thermometer:

120 — 50
100 — 40
80 — 30
   — 20
60 — 10
40 — 0
20 — 10
0 — 20
20 — 30
40 — 40

°F   °C

1 Ⓐ Ⓑ Ⓒ Ⓓ   4 Ⓐ Ⓑ Ⓒ Ⓓ   7 Ⓐ Ⓑ Ⓒ Ⓓ   10 Ⓐ Ⓑ Ⓒ Ⓓ

2 Ⓐ Ⓑ Ⓒ Ⓓ   5 Ⓐ Ⓑ Ⓒ Ⓓ   8 Ⓐ Ⓑ Ⓒ Ⓓ

3 Ⓐ Ⓑ Ⓒ Ⓓ   6 Ⓐ Ⓑ Ⓒ Ⓓ   9 Ⓐ Ⓑ Ⓒ Ⓓ

Go to the next page ⟶

C GRAMMAR IN CONTEXT: Beginning & Ending a Telephone Conversation

Example:

Hello. This is Robert Simon.
_____ to Ms. Harris?
- Ⓐ Can I
- Ⓑ Is she there
- Ⓒ May you speak
- ⬤ May I speak

Thank you.

13. Yes. Please tell _____ that Robert Simon called.
- Ⓐ she
- Ⓑ me
- Ⓒ you
- Ⓓ her

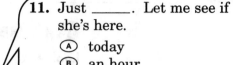

11. Just _____. Let me see if she's here.
- Ⓐ today
- Ⓑ an hour
- Ⓒ you wait
- Ⓓ a moment

12. I'm sorry. She isn't here right now. Can I _____?
- Ⓐ give a message
- Ⓑ give you a message
- Ⓒ take a message
- Ⓓ leave you a message

14. All right. I'll _____.
- Ⓐ give the message
- Ⓑ give her the message
- Ⓒ give you the message
- Ⓓ give me the message

D READING: Telephone Directory White Pages

Look at the telephone listings. Choose the correct answer.

15. What is John Gavin Singleton's phone number?
- Ⓐ 815 267-9534
- Ⓒ 815 495-8197
- Ⓑ 719 389-7283
- Ⓓ 815 459-8197

16. What is Rajdeep Singh's telephone number?
- Ⓐ 719 387-2415
- Ⓒ 815 426-3317
- Ⓑ 815 637-2148
- Ⓓ 815 387-2415

17. What street does Brenda Singer live on?
- Ⓐ Main Street.
- Ⓒ Center Street.
- Ⓑ Lake Street.
- Ⓓ Central Avenue.

18. What town does Linda live in?
- Ⓐ Wellington.
- Ⓒ Willston.
- Ⓑ Holbrook.
- Ⓓ Hopedale.

19. What town does Dennis Singleton live in?
- Ⓐ Arlington.
- Ⓒ Willston.
- Ⓑ Wellington.
- Ⓓ Holbrook.

SINCLAIR—SINGLETON	649
SINGER Alexander 42 Lake Nor 815 427-7251	
Dennis 143 Main Arl 815 639-9148	
Tom & Brenda 1423 Central Wil 719 825-1491	
SINGH Hardeep 753 Pond Arl 815 637-2148	
Madan 2213 River Nor 815 426-3317	
R 1719 School Hol 719 387-2415	
SINGLER Linda 27 Oak Wil 719 828-4124	
SINGLETON D 819 Shore Wel 815 267-9534	
John E 238 Maple Hol 719 389-7283	
John G 12 Adams Hop 815 495-8197	

RESIDENCE LISTING

••

11	Ⓐ Ⓑ Ⓒ Ⓓ	14	Ⓐ Ⓑ Ⓒ Ⓓ	17	Ⓐ Ⓑ Ⓒ Ⓓ
12	Ⓐ Ⓑ Ⓒ Ⓓ	15	Ⓐ Ⓑ Ⓒ Ⓓ	18	Ⓐ Ⓑ Ⓒ Ⓓ
13	Ⓐ Ⓑ Ⓒ Ⓓ	16	Ⓐ Ⓑ Ⓒ Ⓓ	19	Ⓐ Ⓑ Ⓒ Ⓓ

NORTHBORO TOWN OF

AMBULANCE
Emergency Only 911
ANIMAL CONTROL 815 821-6014
BOARD OF HEALTH 815 821-6020
ELECTRIC LIGHT DEPT 815 821-6035
HIGHWAY DEPT 815 821-6040
LIBRARY 400 Main Nor 815 821-6030
PARKS & RECREATION 815 821-6018
POLICE—
Emergency Only 911
All Other Purposes 815 821-5000
SCHOOLS—
Elementary—
Eastwick 360 Main Nor 815 821-6130
Middle School—
Jefferson 120 Central Nor 815 821-6140
High School—
Lincoln 72 School Nor 815 821-6180

20. The street lamp on Hernan's street is broken. What number should he call?

- Ⓐ 911
- Ⓑ 815 821-5000
- Ⓒ 815 821-6014
- Ⓓ 815 821-6035

21. A very mean dog is running up and down the street in front of Claudia's apartment building. What number should she call?

- Ⓐ 815 821-6020
- Ⓑ 815 821-6018
- Ⓒ 815 821-6040
- Ⓓ 815 821-6014

22. The Chungs just moved to Northboro. They want to enroll their son in 10th grade. What number should they call?

- Ⓐ 815 821-6180
- Ⓑ 815 621-6140
- Ⓒ 815 821-6130
- Ⓓ 815 821-6060

23. The Hills ate at a restaurant yesterday. This morning they all have terrible stomachaches. They think the chicken at the restaurant was bad. What number should they call?

- Ⓐ 815 821-6014
- Ⓑ 815 821-6030
- Ⓒ 815 821-6020
- Ⓓ 815 821-5000

24. There's broken glass in the playground across the street from the police station. What number should you call?

- Ⓐ 815 821-6130
- Ⓑ 815 821-6018
- Ⓒ 815 821-5000
- Ⓓ 911

► **Pizza**

Classic Pizza & Pasta
124 Main Ple 315 469-7750
Jimmy's House of Pizza
32 Western Ree 315 727-9123

► **Plants—Retail**

Flowers For You
1200 Central Ree 315 727-4124

► **Plumbing Contractors**

AJAX Plumbing
See Our Display Ad Page 307
1450 Central Ree 315 729-4000
DUFFY & SONS
632 Lake Wat 418 274-1234
Landry Plumbing & Heating
27 Pine Wal 418 829-3600
Reliable Plumbing
4250 Lawson Wol 315 643-2121

25. What is the phone number of the pizza shop in Pleasantville?

- Ⓐ 315 727-9123
- Ⓑ 315 469-7750
- Ⓒ 315 727-9213
- Ⓓ 315 469-7550

26. Which town in this area has a place to buy plants and flowers?

- Ⓐ Retail
- Ⓑ Centerville
- Ⓒ Remington
- Ⓓ Reedsville

27. What's the telephone number of the plumbing company in Watertown?

- Ⓐ 315 729-4000
- Ⓑ 418 829-3600
- Ⓒ 418 274-1234
- Ⓓ 315 643-2121

28. Where is the Ajax Plumbing Company located?

- Ⓐ On page 307.
- Ⓑ In Remington.
- Ⓒ On Central Ave.
- Ⓓ 315 729-4000.

29. You live in Wallingford, and you need a plumber right away! What number should you call for the closest plumber?

- Ⓐ 315 643-2121
- Ⓑ 418 829-3600
- Ⓒ 418 274-1234
- Ⓓ 315 729-4000

20 Ⓐ Ⓑ Ⓒ Ⓓ   23 Ⓐ Ⓑ Ⓒ Ⓓ   26 Ⓐ Ⓑ Ⓒ Ⓓ   29 Ⓐ Ⓑ Ⓒ Ⓓ

21 Ⓐ Ⓑ Ⓒ Ⓓ   24 Ⓐ Ⓑ Ⓒ Ⓓ   27 Ⓐ Ⓑ Ⓒ Ⓓ

22 Ⓐ Ⓑ Ⓒ Ⓓ   25 Ⓐ Ⓑ Ⓒ Ⓓ   28 Ⓐ Ⓑ Ⓒ Ⓓ

Go to the next page ⟩

F CLOZE READING: Phone Messages

Choose the correct answers to complete the messages.

Mom [call (A)] [calls (B)] [called (●)] at 4:00. She [has (A)] [have (B)] [having (C)] ³⁰ to work late at the

office this evening. [She (A)] [She'll (B)] [She's (C)] ³¹ be home at about 9 PM.

Mr. Slate called [to (A)] [from (B)] [through (C)] ³² the garage about your car repairs. You should call

[us (A)] [her (B)] [him (C)] ³³ as soon as possible.

Grandma and Grandpa called to [speak (A)] [tell (B)] [say (C)] ³⁴ hello. [We're (A)] [They're (B)] [You're (C)] ³⁵

fine, and you don't have to call [them (A)] [they (B)] [their (C)] ³⁶ back.

G LISTENING ASSESSMENT: Recorded Telephone Information

Read and listen to the questions. Then listen to the library's recorded announcements and answer the questions.

37. When does the book club meet?
   (A) On the 1st Tuesday of each month.
   (B) On the 3rd Tuesday of each month.
   (C) On the 1st Thursday of each month.
   (D) On the 3rd Thursday of each month.

38. How many evening programs are there each month?
   (A) One.
   (B) Two.
   (C) Three.
   (D) Four.

39. How many hours is the library open on Wednesdays?
   (A) 4 hours.
   (B) 6 hours.
   (C) 9 hours.
   (D) 12 hours.

40. On which date will the children's story hour meet?
   (A) March 5.
   (B) March 12.
   (C) March 19.
   (D) March 26.

H WRITING ASSESSMENT

Write about how you use the telephone. Do you use the telephone for work or for school? Do you talk to family members or friends in other places? Who do you talk to? How often? (Use a separate sheet of paper.)

I SPEAKING ASSESSMENT

I can call someone and answer the phone using these expressions:

Call Answer

☐ ☐ Hello. This is _____. May I please speak to _____?
☐ ☐ _____ isn't here right now. Can I take a message?
☐ ☐ Yes. Please tell _____ that _____.

....

30 (A) (B) (C) (D)   33 (A) (B) (C) (D)   36 (A) (B) (C) (D)   39 (A) (B) (C) (D)

31 (A) (B) (C) (D)   34 (A) (B) (C) (D)   37 (A) (B) (C) (D)   40 (A) (B) (C) (D)

32 (A) (B) (C) (D)   35 (A) (B) (C) (D)   38 (A) (B) (C) (D)

STOP

A HOUSEHOLD REPAIR PROBLEMS

Choose the correct answer to complete the conversation.

1. My washing machine is broken.
   You should call _____.
   - Ⓐ a TV repairperson
   - Ⓑ an appliance repairperson
   - Ⓒ an electrician
   - Ⓓ a plumber

2. Somebody stole the keys to my apartment.
   You should call _____.
   - Ⓐ a carpenter
   - Ⓑ a plumber
   - Ⓒ a painter
   - Ⓓ a locksmith

3. Smoke comes into the room when we use
   the fireplace.
   You should call _____.
   - Ⓐ a chimneysweep
   - Ⓑ the fire department
   - Ⓒ a carpenter
   - Ⓓ a painter

4. Channels 2 through 50 are okay, but
   Channels 51 through 100 have a very
   bad picture.
   We should call _____.
   - Ⓐ an electrician
   - Ⓑ an appliance repairperson
   - Ⓒ a TV repairperson
   - Ⓓ the cable TV company

5. Look at all these bugs!
   We should call _____.
   - Ⓐ an electrician
   - Ⓑ the animal control officer
   - Ⓒ an exterminator
   - Ⓓ the zoo

6. I couldn't fix the doorbell.
   Let's call _____.
   - Ⓐ a locksmith
   - Ⓑ an electrician
   - Ⓒ an appliance repairperson
   - Ⓓ a mechanic

B GRAMMAR IN CONTEXT: Securing Household Repair Services

Choose the correct answer to complete the conversation.

7. There's _____ wrong with
   my bathroom sink. Can
   you send _____ to fix it?
   - Ⓐ anything . . . anyone
   - Ⓑ anyone . . . anything
   - Ⓒ something . . . someone
   - Ⓓ someone . . . something

8. I can't send _____ today.
   Will _____ be home
   tomorrow at 10 AM?
   - Ⓐ somebody . . . somebody
   - Ⓑ anybody . . . anything
   - Ⓒ anybody . . . somebody
   - Ⓓ anything . . . something

9. I _____ be home at ten, but
   _____ be back at eleven.
   Is 11:00 okay?
   - Ⓐ won't . . . I'll
   - Ⓑ won't . . . you'll
   - Ⓒ will . . . I'll
   - Ⓓ will . . . you'll

10. Yes. _____ will be there
    at eleven.
    - Ⓐ Anything
    - Ⓑ Anybody
    - Ⓒ Something
    - Ⓓ Someone

1 Ⓐ Ⓑ Ⓒ Ⓓ   3 Ⓐ Ⓑ Ⓒ Ⓓ   6 Ⓐ Ⓑ Ⓒ Ⓓ   9 Ⓐ Ⓑ Ⓒ Ⓓ

2 Ⓐ Ⓑ Ⓒ Ⓓ   4 Ⓐ Ⓑ Ⓒ Ⓓ   7 Ⓐ Ⓑ Ⓒ Ⓓ   10 Ⓐ Ⓑ Ⓒ Ⓓ

                5 Ⓐ Ⓑ Ⓒ Ⓓ   8 Ⓐ Ⓑ Ⓒ Ⓓ

Go to the next page ▷

Look at the TV listings. Choose the correct answer.

	6:00	6:30	7:00	7:30	8:00	8:30	9:00	9:30	10:00	10:30
2	News at 6 (News)	CBS Evening News (News)	Entertainment Tonight (Talk/Tabloid)	Who Wants to be a Millionaire (Game)	Life with Bobby: *Out to Lunch* (Comedy)	Everybody Loves Richard: *The Love Letter* (Comedy)	FBI Special Investigations Unit: *The Dangerous Package* (Crime)		PrimeTime Monday (Talk/Tabloid)	
4	Channel 4 News (News)	NBC Nightly News (News)	EXTRA (Talk/Tabloid)	Access Hollywood (Talk/Tabloid)	Happiest Class: *A New Teacher* (Comedy)	Wanda: *A Visitor from the Past* (Comedy)	Fletcher: *Bob's New Diet* (Comedy)	Fletcher: *Eat Your Vegetables* (Comedy)	Law & Order: *Bad Day at the Bank* (Crime)	
5	Everybody Loves Richard: *The First Day* (Comedy)	Everybody Loves Richard: *A New Friend* (Comedy)	Walt & Grace: *The Argument* (Comedy)	Neighbors: *The Lost Dog* (Comedy)	Biltmore Boys: *Alan's Problem* (Drama)		Three Sisters: *Trisha's New Boss* (Drama)		News at Ten (News)	
7	Eyewitness News (News)	ABC World News Tonight (News)	Jeopardy! (Game)	Wheel of Fortune (Game)	I'm With You: *Lost at the Mall* (Comedy)	Two by Two: *The School Dance* (Comedy)	According to Amy: *The Phone Message* (Comedy)	Better Than Ever: *Jim's New Couch* (Comedy)	LAPD Red: *Fight on the Freeway* (Crime)	
9	Baseball: *Anaheim Angels at Texas Rangers* (Sports) (Live)				KCAL 9 News at 8:00 PM		KCAL 9 News at 9:00 PM		KCAL 9 News at 10:00 PM (News)	Sports Central (News)
11	The Sampsons: *You're Fired!* (Cartoon)	Queen of the Hill: *Sally's New Car* (Comedy)	The Prince of Long Beach: *The Car Accident* (Comedy)	The Sampsons: *Henry's New Job* (Cartoon)	Downtown Medical Center: *Bad Day in the ER* (Reality)		Lost on an Island (Reality)		Fox 11 Ten O'Clock News (News)	
22	Cuanto Cuesta el Show (Game)		Noticias 22 (News)	El Tribunal del Pueblo (Reality)	El Hijo de Pedro Navajas (1986, Spanish)				Noticias 22 (News)	Contacto Deportivo (Sports/Info)
28	The NewsHour (News/Talk)		California's Golden Parks (Nature)	In the Kitchen (Cooking)	This Old Apartment: *Chicago* (Home Repair)		Great Performances: *Boston Symphony Orchestra in Moscow* (Concert)		NOVA: *Bugs, Bugs, Bugs* (Science)	

11. What's on Channel 5 at 7:00?
- Ⓐ *EXTRA.*
- Ⓑ *Walt & Grace.*
- Ⓒ *Jeopardy!*
- Ⓓ *Wheel of Fortune.*

12. What time is *Two by Two* on today?
- Ⓐ 8:00.
- Ⓑ 8:30.
- Ⓒ Channel 2.
- Ⓓ Channel 7.

13. What's on Channel 2 at 7:30?
- Ⓐ A game show.
- Ⓑ A comedy show.
- Ⓒ A news program.
- Ⓓ A cartoon program.

14. Which channel has programs in Spanish?
- Ⓐ Channel 5.
- Ⓑ Channel 11.
- Ⓒ Channel 22.
- Ⓓ Channel 28.

15. How many channels show the program *Everybody Loves Richard?*
- Ⓐ One.
- Ⓑ Two.
- Ⓒ Three.
- Ⓓ Four.

16. Which channels have news programs at 10:00?
- Ⓐ 2, 4, 7.
- Ⓑ 2, 4, 7, 28.
- Ⓒ 5, 9, 11.
- Ⓓ 5, 9, 11, 22.

17. My aunt loves classical music. What time is she going to watch TV today?
- Ⓐ 7:00.
- Ⓑ 8:00.
- Ⓒ 9:00.
- Ⓓ 10:00.

18. How many crime shows are on TV this evening?
- Ⓐ One.
- Ⓑ Two.
- Ⓒ Three.
- Ⓓ Four.

19. Which channel has the most news programs?
- Ⓐ Channel 2.
- Ⓑ Channel 4.
- Ⓒ Channel 7.
- Ⓓ Channel 9.

20. Which program isn't on tonight?
- Ⓐ *Neighbors.*
- Ⓑ *Friends.*
- Ⓒ *NOVA.*
- Ⓓ *LAPD Red.*

. . . .

11 Ⓐ Ⓑ Ⓒ Ⓓ   13 Ⓐ Ⓑ Ⓒ Ⓓ   16 Ⓐ Ⓑ Ⓒ Ⓓ   19 Ⓐ Ⓑ Ⓒ Ⓓ

12 Ⓐ Ⓑ Ⓒ Ⓓ   14 Ⓐ Ⓑ Ⓒ Ⓓ   17 Ⓐ Ⓑ Ⓒ Ⓓ   20 Ⓐ Ⓑ Ⓒ Ⓓ

D CLOZE READING: Household Repairs & Pronoun Review

Choose the correct answers to complete the story.

My brother is very upset. **She He We**[_] is having a problem in **him his he** ²¹ apartment.
(A) (●) (C)   (A) (B) (C)

He Him His ²² oven is broken. **He It She** ²³ doesn't go on. My brother tried to fix it
(A) (B) (C)   (A) (B) (C)

itself hisself himself ²⁴, but he couldn't. He called the building manager a few days ago.
(A) (B) (C)

She Her Hers ²⁵ wasn't there, so **it she he** ²⁶ left a message on **she her hers** ²⁷
(A) (B) (C)   (A) (B) (C)   (A) (B) (C)

answering machine. **He's His It's** ²⁸ still waiting for **her she hers** ²⁹ to call back. So while
(A) (B) (C)   (A) (B) (C)

my brother's oven is broken, **it she he** ³⁰ comes over to **my me mine** ³¹ apartment and
(A) (B) (C)   (A) (B) (C)

uses **my mine me** ³². I'm happy to help **him his he** ³³. After all, he's **me my mine** ³⁴
(A) (B) (C)   (A) (B) (C)   (A) (B) (C)

brother!

E LISTENING ASSESSMENT: Recorded Telephone Instructions

Read and listen to the questions. Then listen to the telephone instructions and answer the questions.

35. Marina wants to fly from Los Angeles to Madrid, Spain. Which key should she press?
- (A) 1
- (B) 2
- (C) 3
- (D) 4

36. Roger wants to fly from Houston to Miami. Which key should he press?
- (A) 1
- (B) 2
- (C) 3
- (D) 4

37. Grace wants to make flight and hotel reservations for a tour of Italy. Which key should she press?
- (A) 1
- (B) 2
- (C) 3
- (D) 4

38. Daniel is looking for a job as a flight attendant. Which key should he press?
- (A) *
- (B) 1
- (C) 3
- (D) 5

39. Karen didn't hear the first two instructions. Which key should she press?
- (A) *
- (B) 1
- (C) 4
- (D) 5

40. Joseph is going to fly to New York tonight. Will his plane leave on time? Which key should he press?
- (A) *
- (B) 1
- (C) 2
- (D) 5

....

21 (A) (B) (C) (D)	27 (A) (B) (C) (D)	33 (A) (B) (C) (D)	39 (A) (B) (C) (D)
22 (A) (B) (C) (D)	28 (A) (B) (C) (D)	34 (A) (B) (C) (D)	40 (A) (B) (C) (D)
23 (A) (B) (C) (D)	29 (A) (B) (C) (D)	35 (A) (B) (C) (D)	
24 (A) (B) (C) (D)	30 (A) (B) (C) (D)	36 (A) (B) (C) (D)	
25 (A) (B) (C) (D)	31 (A) (B) (C) (D)	37 (A) (B) (C) (D)	
26 (A) (B) (C) (D)	32 (A) (B) (C) (D)	38 (A) (B) (C) (D)	

Go to the next page ⇒

Fill out the chart with your schedule for a typical week. Write in your times at school, at work, at meetings, and at other events. Also write in the things you do to relax, including sports, favorite TV shows, and other evening and weekend activities

	MON	TUE	WED	THU	FRI	SAT	SUN
6:00 AM							
7:00							
8:00							
9:00							
10:00							
11:00							
12:00 Noon							
1:00 PM							
2:00							
3:00							
4:00							
5:00							
6:00							
7:00							
8:00							
9:00							
10:00							
11:00							

G SPEAKING ASSESSMENT

I can ask and answer these questions:

Ask Answer
- ☐ ☐ When there's something wrong with an appliance in your apartment or home, who fixes it?
- ☐ ☐ Do you like to fix things?
- ☐ ☐ What can you fix?

Ask Answer
- ☐ ☐ Tell about your typical schedule during the week.
- ☐ ☐ Tell about your typical schedule on the weekend.
- ☐ ☐ What TV programs do you usually watch? When?

STOP

Side by Side Plus 2
Unit Achievement Tests Listening Script

UNIT 1 TEST
Section G

Read and listen to the questions.

  38. What's his address?
  39. When is his birthday?
  40. How tall is he?

Now listen to the interview, and answer the questions.

  A. What's your name?
  B. Victor Sanchez.
  A. What's your address?
  B. 94 Center Street in Reedville.
  A. And your telephone number?
  B. (978) 583-4712.
  A. What's your date of birth?
  B. May thirteenth, nineteen eighty-three.
  A. And what's your height?
  B. I'm five feet eight inches tall.

UNIT 2 TEST
Section G

Read and listen to the questions.

  38. When DOESN'T the school have English classes?
  39. Where is Wendy going to write her personal information?
  40. At what time AREN'T there any classes at this school?

Now listen to the conversation, and answer the questions.

  A. May I help you?
  B. Yes. My name is Wendy Chen. I want to study English. Do you have English classes at this school?
  A. Yes, we do. We have classes five days a week, Monday through Friday, in the morning and in the evening. Here's a registration form. Please print all your personal information in ink. Do you have a pen?
  B. Yes, I do.
  A. And do you have a document with your address?
  B. Yes. I have a driver's license.

  A. Good. Complete the form. Then give me the form and show me your driver's license. Then you're going to take a short English test.
  B. Okay. Thank you.

UNIT 3 TEST
Section H

Read and listen to the questions.

  38. Where is the conversation taking place?
  39. What is the customer going to have for an appetizer?
  40. How many side orders is the customer going to have?

Now listen to the conversation, and answer the questions.

  A. Are you ready to order?
  B. Yes, I am. I'd like the baked chicken, please.
  A. All right. And what side order are you going to have with that?
  B. Let me have an order of rice and an order of carrots, please.
  A. Do you want a salad with your meal?
  B. No, I don't think so.
  A. And do you want to start with an appetizer this evening?
  B. Let me see. Yes. Please give me a bowl of vegetable soup.
  A. Anything to drink?
  B. Yes. A glass of milk, please.

UNIT 4 TEST
Section E

Read and listen to the questions.

  38. What day is it?
  39. What are they going to do tomorrow?
  40. Where are they going to meet?

Now listen to the conversation, and answer the questions.

  A. Would you like to have dinner with me after work today?
  B. I'm sorry. I can't. I go to a computer class every Tuesday after work.

A. How about tomorrow? Would you like to have dinner tomorrow?
B. Tomorrow? Yes. I'd love to.
A. Great. I'll meet you at five at your office. Okay?
B. Great.

UNIT 5 TEST

Section E

Read and listen to the questions.

38. What do they disagree about?
39. What do they agree about?
40. Which opinion do they probably agree about?

Now listen to the conversation, and answer the questions.

A. You know, I think the streets in our city aren't as clean as they used to be.
B. I think so, too. But I think the buildings in our city are very interesting.
A. Do you really think so? In my opinion, the buildings in other cities around here are MORE interesting.
B. What do you think about the people in our city?
A. I think they're very friendly. Do you agree?
B. Definitely. And I think our parks are very beautiful.
A. I don't think so.

UNIT 6 TEST

Section G

Read and listen to the questions.

38. How many items does the person want to return?
39. What's the matter with the shirt?
40. Where is the conversation taking place?

Now listen to the conversation, and answer the questions.

A. May I help you?
B. Yes, please. I want to return this shirt and this pair of pants.
A. What's the matter with them?
B. The shirt is too small, and the pants are too large.
A. I see. Do you want to exchange them?
B. No. I just want to return them, please.

A. All right. I'm afraid you can't return items here in the Men's Clothing department. You can return them at the Customer Service counter.
B. Where is that?
A. It's downstairs on the first floor next to the elevator.
B. Okay. Thanks very much.

UNIT 7 TEST

Section H

Read and listen to the questions.

37. In which direction is the post office?
38. In which direction is the library?
39. In which direction is the shopping mall?
40. In which direction is the zoo?

Now listen to the conversation, and answer the questions.

A. Excuse me. I'm new here in town. Would you please tell me how to get to the post office from here?
B. Sure. Drive east along this street about three blocks and you'll see the post office on the right.
A. And could you please tell me how to get to the nearest shopping mall from here?
B. Yes. It's very easy. Turn left at the next street and then drive south for about two miles. The shopping mall is across from the airport.
A. Is there a library near here?
B. Yes. There's a brand new library about ten blocks from here. Just turn right and drive west along School Street, and you'll see the library across from the high school.
A. And can you recommend a place to go with my children?
B. Yes. We have a wonderful zoo.
A. Is it very far?
B. Not at all. It's about two miles north of here.
A. Well, thank you very much.
B. No problem. And welcome to Greenville!

UNIT 8 TEST

Section H

Read and listen to the questions.

38. What kind of position is the person applying for?
39. Where is the conversation taking place?
40. How many years of work experience does the applicant have?

Now listen to the conversation, and answer the questions.

A. Tell me about your skills.
B. I can type, and I can file.
A. Do you know how to use accounting software on a computer?
B. Yes. I used accounting software in my previous job.
A. Where was that?
B. I worked at the Johnson Insurance Company.
A. How long did you work there?
B. For three years.
A. And where did you work before that?
B. I worked at the Larsen Real Estate agency for two years, and before that I worked as a cashier at the Citywide Supermarket for one year.
A. And why are you interested in a position with us at Landmark Data Management?
B. I know this is an excellent company, and I think that I can be a very effective and useful employee here.

UNIT 9 TEST

Section G

Read and listen to the questions.

38. When did the person fall?
39. What's their address?
40. Where is their apartment?

Now listen to the conversation, and answer the questions.

A. Emergency Operator.
B. I want to report an emergency.
A. Yes. Go ahead.
B. My mother tripped and fell while she was walking down the stairs in our building. She can't speak to me.
A. What's your address?
B. 30 East Street in Westville.
A. Is that an apartment building or a home?
B. An apartment building. We're on the sixth floor in Apartment 6-D.

A. Okay. Stay with your mother but don't move her. An ambulance is on the way.
B. Thank you.

UNIT 10 TEST

Section E

Read and listen to the questions.

37. Where is the one-bedroom apartment?
38. How much is the rent on the two-bedroom unit?
39. Which pets are allowed in the building?
40. How much is the security deposit on the one-bedroom apartment?

Now listen to the telephone conversation, and answer the questions.

A. City Square Apartments. May I help you?
B. Yes. Do you have any apartments available?
A. Yes, we do. We currently have two apartments available. We have a one-bedroom unit on the fifth floor, and we have a two-bedroom unit on the sixth floor.
B. I see. And how much is the rent?
A. The apartment on the sixth floor is $1,100 per month. The one-bedroom rents for $800 per month.
B. Is there a security deposit?
A. Yes. A deposit of two months' rent is required when you sign the lease.
B. Are pets allowed in the building?
A. Cats and smaller pets are allowed, but not dogs.
B. And is there an elevator in the building?
A. Yes. There are two. Would you like to make an appointment to see the units?
B. Yes, please.

UNIT 11 TEST

Section I

Read and listen to the questions.

38. When did she hurt her back?
39. Where did she hurt it?
40. What time does she have to be at the clinic?

Now listen to the conversation, and answer the questions.

A. Midtown Clinic.
B. Hello. I'd like to make an appointment, please.

A. What seems to be the problem?
B. I have a very bad backache.
A. I see. And when did your back begin to hurt?
B. Last Tuesday. I hurt it while I was moving some heavy boxes in the supply room at work.
A. Can you come in on Thursday morning at 7:30?
B. 7:30? Yes.
A. What's the name?
B. Veronica Matthews.
A. Telephone number?
B. (916) 728-9236.
A. Do you have medical insurance?
B. Yes.
A. And will this be your first visit to the Midtown Clinic?
B. Yes, it will.
A. Then please plan to arrive for your appointment fifteen minutes early to fill out a medical history form.
B. Fifteen minutes early? All right.
A. We'll see you on Thursday, Ms. Matthews.
B. Thank you.

UNIT 12 TEST

Section G

Read and listen to the questions.

37. When does the book club meet?
38. How many evening programs are there each month?
39. How many hours is the library open on Wednesdays?
40. On which date will the children's story hour meet?

Now listen to the library's recorded announcements, and answer the questions.

This is the Central Library community events line. Here is the current listing of community events at the library. On the first Saturday of each month at 9 AM, children ages four to ten are invited to our children's story hour. On the third Thursday of each month, join librarian Kate Winters for the lunchtime book club. It meets in the community room at twelve noon. On the second and fourth Tuesdays of each month, come to our evening programs to learn about new books in the library collection. The programs start at 7:30. The Central Library is open Monday through Friday from 9 AM to 9 PM, Saturday from 9 AM to 6 PM, and Sunday from 1 PM to 5 PM. Thank you for calling the Central Library community events line. Have a good day.

UNIT 13 TEST

Section E

Read and listen to the questions.

35. Marina wants to fly from Los Angeles to Madrid, Spain. Which key should she press?
36. Roger wants to fly from Houston to Miami. Which key should he press?
37. Grace wants to make flight and hotel reservations for a tour of Italy. Which key should she press?
38. Daniel is looking for a job as a flight attendant. Which key should he press?
39. Karen didn't hear the first two instructions. Which key should she press?
40. Joseph is going to fly to New York tonight. Will his plane leave on time? Which key should he press?

Now listen to the telephone instructions, and answer the questions.

Thank you for calling National Airlines. Please make your selection from the following menu. For automated flight departure and arrival information, press 1. For travel reservations within the United States, press 2. For international travel reservations, press 3. For vacation packages, press 4. For all other information, press 5. To repeat this menu, press the star key.

SIDE BY SIDE PLUS 2

Unit Achievement Tests Answer Sheet

UNIT _____

Student's Name _____ I.D. Number _____

Course _____ Teacher _____ Date _____

1 (A) (B) (C) (D)   21 (A) (B) (C) (D)
2 (A) (B) (C) (D)   22 (A) (B) (C) (D)
3 (A) (B) (C) (D)   23 (A) (B) (C) (D)
4 (A) (B) (C) (D)   24 (A) (B) (C) (D)
5 (A) (B) (C) (D)   25 (A) (B) (C) (D)
6 (A) (B) (C) (D)   26 (A) (B) (C) (D)
7 (A) (B) (C) (D)   27 (A) (B) (C) (D)
8 (A) (B) (C) (D)   28 (A) (B) (C) (D)
9 (A) (B) (C) (D)   29 (A) (B) (C) (D)
10 (A) (B) (C) (D)   30 (A) (B) (C) (D)
11 (A) (B) (C) (D)   31 (A) (B) (C) (D)
12 (A) (B) (C) (D)   32 (A) (B) (C) (D)
13 (A) (B) (C) (D)   33 (A) (B) (C) (D)
14 (A) (B) (C) (D)   34 (A) (B) (C) (D)
15 (A) (B) (C) (D)   35 (A) (B) (C) (D)
16 (A) (B) (C) (D)   36 (A) (B) (C) (D)
17 (A) (B) (C) (D)   37 (A) (B) (C) (D)
18 (A) (B) (C) (D)   38 (A) (B) (C) (D)
19 (A) (B) (C) (D)   39 (A) (B) (C) (D)
20 (A) (B) (C) (D)   40 (A) (B) (C) (D)

Side by Side Plus 2
Unit Achievement Tests Answer Key

UNIT 1 TEST

A–G.

1. D	11. A	21. A	31. A
2. B	12. C	22. B	32. A
3. D	13. D	23. C	33. B
4. A	14. B	24. A	34. C
5. C	15. C	25. D	35. C
6. B	16. B	26. B	36. B
7. C	17. A	27. C	37. A
8. A	18. D	28. A	38. D
9. D	19. D	29. C	39. B
10. B	20. C	30. B	40. C

H. MONTHS, DAYS, & DATES

November	July	January
August	June	February
March	April	May
September	October	December
Monday	Friday	Sunday
Wednesday	Saturday	Tuesday
Thursday		

I. ORDINAL NUMBERS

2nd	17th	sixth
9th	31st	fifteenth
1st	53rd	twenty-first
12th	85th	ninety-second

UNIT 2 TEST

A–G.

1. C	11. B	21. C	31. C
2. A	12. C	22. B	32. B
3. D	13. A	23. B	33. B
4. B	14. D	24. A	34. A
5. C	15. A	25. D	35. A
6. D	16. B	26. C	36. C
7. A	17. C	27. A	37. A
8. C	18. D	28. B	38. D
9. B	19. B	29. C	39. B
10. D	20. A	30. D	40. C

H. LEARNING SKILLS

4	4
6	2
1	6
3	3
2	5
5	1

UNIT 3 TEST

A–H.

1. A	11. D	21. D	31. C
2. D	12. B	22. B	32. C
3. B	13. D	23. C	33. A
4. C	14. C	24. D	34. D
5. D	15. A	25. A	35. A
6. C	16. D	26. C	36. C
7. A	17. C	27. B	37. B
8. C	18. B	28. A	38. B
9. B	19. A	29. B	39. D
10. A	20. C	30. D	40. C

UNIT 4 TEST

A–E.

1. C	11. B	21. B	31. A
2. B	12. A	22. D	32. C
3. D	13. D	23. A	33. B
4. A	14. C	24. D	34. B
5. B	15. D	25. C	35. B
6. C	16. A	26. B	36. C
7. D	17. C	27. A	37. A
8. A	18. B	28. D	38. A
9. C	19. D	29. C	39. B
10. B	20. C	30. D	40. D

UNIT 5 TEST

A–E.

1. C	11. B	21. A	31. B
2. B	12. C	22. B	32. B
3. A	13. A	23. D	33. A
4. C	14. B	24. C	34. C
5. D	15. D	25. B	35. C
6. B	16. A	26. A	36. B
7. C	17. C	27. B	37. A
8. A	18. C	28. D	38. A
9. D	19. B	29. C	39. D
10. D	20. D	30. A	40. C

UNIT 6 TEST

A–G.

1. C	11. C	21. A	31. D
2. B	12. D	22. D	32. C
3. A	13. B	23. C	33. C
4. A	14. A	24. D	34. A
5. C	15. B	25. B	35. B
6. D	16. A	26. A	36. B
7. D	17. C	27. C	37. A
8. C	18. D	28. D	38. B
9. B	19. C	29. B	39. C
10. A	20. B	30. A	40. D

H. WRITING ASSESSMENT

		1024
		(Date)
Pay to the order of Metrovision Cable TV	$	24.95
Twenty-four dollars and 95/100 . . .		Dollars
For Cable TV Service	(Signature)	
057009345 200042534 1024		

I. LEARNING SKILL

3

6

1

4

2

5

UNIT 7 TEST

A–H.

1. B	11. A	21. B	31. C
2. A	12. D	22. B	32. B
3. B	13. A	23. A	33. C
4. C	14. C	24. C	34. A
5. D	15. D	25. C	35. B
6. A	16. C	26. D	36. C
7. B	17. D	27. B	37. C
8. C	18. B	28. A	38. D
9. D	19. A	29. C	39. B
10. B	20. D	30. D	40. A

UNIT 8 TEST

A–H.

1. C	11. B	21. D	31. A
2. D	12. A	22. B	32. D
3. B	13. D	23. C	33. B
4. A	14. C	24. C	34. B
5. C	15. C	25. D	35. C
6. D	16. D	26. B	36. B
7. B	17. A	27. C	37. A
8. C	18. B	28. D	38. B
9. B	19. C	29. A	39. C
10. A	20. A	30. B	40. D

UNIT 9 TEST

A–G.

1. B	11. C	21. D	31. A
2. A	12. B	22. C	32. B
3. D	13. A	23. C	33. D
4. C	14. D	24. C	34. A
5. D	15. C	25. B	35. C
6. A	16. B	26. D	36. B
7. B	17. C	27. A	37. A
8. A	18. D	28. C	38. D
9. C	19. A	29. D	39. C
10. D	20. B	30. B	40. B

UNIT 10 TEST

A–E.

1. B	11. C	21. B	31. A
2. D	12. B	22. C	32. D
3. A	13. D	23. D	33. C
4. C	14. A	24. A	34. D
5. D	15. C	25. C	35. B
6. B	16. D	26. B	36. A
7. A	17. B	27. B	37. C
8. D	18. A	28. A	38. D
9. A	19. D	29. D	39. B
10. B	20. C	30. C	40. C

UNIT 11 TEST

A–I.

1. D	11. B	21. D	31. A
2. B	12. B	22. A	32. B
3. C	13. A	23. B	33. D
4. A	14. C	24. D	34. B
5. C	15. D	25. C	35. B
6. D	16. D	26. D	36. C
7. A	17. A	27. B	37. A
8. B	18. C	28. A	38. C
9. D	19. B	29. C	39. D
10. C	20. C	30. C	40. A

UNIT 12 TEST

A–G.

1. C	11. D	21. D	31. B
2. B	12. C	22. A	32. B
3. A	13. D	23. C	33. C
4. C	14. B	24. B	34. C
5. A	15. C	25. B	35. B
6. B	16. A	26. D	36. A
7. B	17. D	27. C	37. D
8. A	18. C	28. C	38. B
9. B	19. B	29. B	39. D
10. A	20. D	30. A	40. A

UNIT 13 TEST

A–E.

1. B	11. B	21. B	31. A
2. D	12. B	22. C	32. B
3. A	13. A	23. B	33. A
4. D	14. C	24. C	34. B
5. C	15. B	25. A	35. C
6. B	16. D	26. C	36. B
7. C	17. C	27. B	37. D
8. C	18. C	28. A	38. D
9. A	19. D	29. A	39. A
10. D	20. B	30. C	40. B

SIDE BY SIDE PLUS
Learner Assessment Record

BOOK 2 UNIT 1

Student's Name _____ I.D. Number _____

Course _____ Teacher _____ Date _____

Test Sections & Scoring Guidelines/Rubrics: Score:

A–G. MULTIPLE-CHOICE QUESTIONS

Asking Personal Information Questions
Answering Personal Information Questions
Personal Information Form
Grammar in Context: Personal Information
Reading: Calendars, Dates, & Ordinal Numbers
Cloze Reading: Providing Information About Family Members
Listening Assessment: Giving Personal Information

_____ correct x **1** point   _____ (40)

H. MONTHS, DAYS, & DATES

Score **1/2** point for each correct answer. (There are 20 items total.)
(Note: Don't score sample answer.)

_____ correct x **1/2** point   _____ (10)

I. ORDINAL NUMBERS

Score **1** point for each correct answer. (There are 10 items total.)
(Note: Don't score sample answer.)

_____ correct x **1** point   _____ (10)

J. WRITING ASSESSMENT: Personal Information Form

For each form item **except** "Apartment" and "E-mail" (15 items total):
Score **1** if completed correctly.
Score **0** if incorrect or missing.
(Note: Don't score answers for "Apartment" or "E-mail" since some students will need to leave these blank. Maximum number of correct items is 15.)

_____ correct x **2** points   _____ (30)

K. SPEAKING ASSESSMENT

Score <u>separately</u> the student's ability to ask and answer the questions based on appropriateness, grammatical correctness, and comprehensibility:

Score **5** (Excellent), **4** (Good), **3** (Fair), **2** (Poor), or **1** (Unsatisfactory)

Asking the Questions: _____

Answering the Questions: _____   _____ (10)

TOTAL SCORE: _____ (100)

SIDE BY SIDE PLUS
Learner Assessment Record

BOOK **2** UNIT **2**

Student's Name _____   I.D. Number _____

Course _____   Teacher _____   Date _____

Test Sections & Scoring Guidelines/Rubrics: Score:

A–G. MULTIPLE-CHOICE QUESTIONS

School Personnel & Locations
Classroom Instructions
Computer Components
Grammar in Context: School Registration
Reading: A Class Schedule
Cloze Reading: The Education System
Listening Assessment: Registration Procedures

_____ correct x **2** points   _____ (80)

H. LEARNING SKILLS: Chronological Order & Steps in a Process

Score **1/2** point for each correct answer. (There are 10 items total.)
(*Note: Don't score sample answers.*)

_____ correct x **1/2** point   _____ (5)

I. WRITING ASSESSMENT

For each of the following criteria, score **1** (Good) or **0** (Poor):

Appropriateness of content: _____

Spelling: _____

Punctuation & Capitalization: _____

Grammar: _____

Completeness of Sentences: _____   _____ (5)

J. SPEAKING ASSESSMENT

Score <u>separately</u> the student's ability to ask and answer the questions based on appropriateness, grammatical correctness, and comprehensibility:

Score **5** (Excellent), **4** (Good), **3** (Fair), **2** (Poor), or **1** (Unsatisfactory)

Asking the Questions: _____

Answering the Questions: _____   _____ (10)

TOTAL SCORE: _____ (100)

Student's Name _____	I.D. Number _____
Course _____ Teacher _____	Date _____

Test Sections & Scoring Guidelines/Rubrics: Score:

A–H. MULTIPLE-CHOICE QUESTIONS

Food Containers & Quantities
Food Weights & Measures: Abbreviations
Grammar in Context: Asking About Availability & Location of Items
    in a Store
Reading: Food Advertisements
Reading: Food Packaging & Label Information
Reading: A Supermarket Receipt
Reading: Reading a Menu & Computing Costs
Listening Assessment: Ordering a Meal

_____ correct x **2** points   _____ (80)

I. WRITING ASSESSMENT

For each of the following criteria, score **2** (Good), **1** (Fair), or **0** (Unsatisfactory):

Appropriateness of Content: _____

Spelling: _____

Punctuation & Capitalization: _____

Grammar: _____

Completeness of Sentences: _____   _____ (10)

J. SPEAKING ASSESSMENT

Score <u>separately</u> the student's ability to ask and answer the questions based on appropriateness, grammatical correctness, and comprehensibility:

Score **5** (Excellent), **4** (Good), **3** (Fair), **2** (Poor), or **1** (Unsatisfactory)

Asking the Questions: _____

Answering the Questions: _____   _____ (10)

TOTAL SCORE: _____ (100)

SIDE BY SIDE PLUS
Learner Assessment Record

BOOK **2** **UNIT** **4**

Student's Name _____ I.D. Number _____

Course _____ Teacher _____ Date _____

Test Sections & Scoring Guidelines/Rubrics: Score:

A–E. MULTIPLE-CHOICE QUESTIONS

Small Talk at Work & at School
Grammar in Context: Invitations & Offers
Grammar in Context: Asking for Clarification
Cloze Reading: Small Talk at Work
Listening Assessment: An Invitation

_____ correct x **2** points   _____ (80)

F. WRITING ASSESSMENT

For each of the following criteria, score **2** (Good), **1** (Fair), or **0** (Unsatisfactory):

Appropriateness of Content: _____

Spelling: _____

Punctuation & Capitalization: _____

Grammar: _____

Completeness of Sentences: _____   _____ (10)

G. SPEAKING ASSESSMENT

Score <u>separately</u> the student's ability to ask and answer the questions based on appropriateness, grammatical correctness, and comprehensibility:

Score **5** (Excellent), **4** (Good), **3** (Fair), **2** (Poor), or **1** (Unsatisfactory)

Asking the Questions: _____

Answering the Questions: _____   _____ (10)

TOTAL SCORE: _____ (100)

SIDE BY SIDE PLUS
Learner Assessment Record

BOOK **2** UNIT **5**

Student's Name _____ I.D. Number _____

Course _____ Teacher _____ Date _____

Test Sections & Scoring Guidelines/Rubrics: Score:

A–E. MULTIPLE-CHOICE QUESTIONS

Small Talk at Work & at School
Grammar in Context: Compliments
Grammar in Context: Appropriate Language in Social Situations
Cloze Reading: A Thank-You Note
Listening Assessment: Expressing Opinions

_____ correct x **2** points   _____ (80)

F. WRITING ASSESSMENT

For each of the following criteria, score **2** (Good), **1** (Fair), or **0** (Unsatisfactory):

Appropriateness of Content: _____

Spelling: _____

Punctuation & Capitalization: _____

Grammar: _____

Completeness of Sentences: _____   _____ (10)

G. SPEAKING ASSESSMENT

Score <u>separately</u> the student's ability to ask and answer the questions based on appropriateness, grammatical correctness, and comprehensibility:

Score **5** (Excellent), **4** (Good), **3** (Fair), **2** (Poor), or **1** (Unsatisfactory)

Asking the Questions: _____

Answering the Questions: _____   _____ (10)

TOTAL SCORE: _____ (100)

SIDE BY SIDE PLUS
Learner Assessment Record

Student's Name _____ I.D. Number _____

Course _____ Teacher _____ Date _____

Test Sections & Scoring Guidelines/Rubrics: **Score:**

A–G. MULTIPLE-CHOICE QUESTIONS

Shopping Requests & Locating Items
Understanding ATM Instructions
Interpreting a Check
Grammar in Context: Problems with Purchases; Returning an Item
Grammar in Context: Problems with Purchases; Exchanging an Item
Cloze Reading: Store Sales
Listening Assessment: Returning Items

_____ correct x **2** points   _____ (80)

H. WRITING ASSESSMENT: Fill Out the Check

For each of the following lines on the check:
Score **1** if completed correctly.
Score **0** if incorrect or missing.
(Note: Don't score the memo line in the bottom left corner of the check.)

Date: _____

Pay to the order of: _____

Amount in numerals: _____

Amount in words: _____

Signature: _____   _____ (5)

I. LEARNING SKILL: Steps in a Process

Score **1** point for each correct answer.
(Note: Don't score sample answer.)

_____ correct x **1** point   _____ (5)

J. SPEAKING ASSESSMENT

Score <u>separately</u> the student's ability to ask and answer the questions based on appropriateness, grammatical correctness, and comprehensibility:

Score **5** (Excellent), **4** (Good), **3** (Fair), **2** (Poor), or **1** (Unsatisfactory)

Asking the Questions: _____

Answering the Questions: _____   _____ (10)

TOTAL SCORE: _____ (100)

Test Sections & Scoring Guidelines/Rubrics: Score:

A–H. MULTIPLE-CHOICE QUESTIONS

Schedules
Locating Places on a Map
Reading: A Bus Schedule
Highway & Traffic Signs & Symbols
Police Commands & Traffic Signs
Grammar in Context: Postal Services
Cloze Reading: Simple Written Directions
Listening Assessment: Compass Directions

_____ correct x **2** points   _____ (80)

I. WRITING ASSESSMENT

For each of the following criteria, score **2** (Good), **1** (Fair), or **0** (Unsatisfactory):

Quality of map drawn by student: _____

Spelling: _____

Punctuation & Capitalization: _____

Grammar: _____

Completeness of Sentences: _____   _____ (10)

J. SPEAKING ASSESSMENT

Score <u>separately</u> the student's ability to ask and answer the questions based on appropriateness, grammatical correctness, and comprehensibility:

Score **5** (Excellent), **4** (Good), **3** (Fair), **2** (Poor), or **1** (Unsatisfactory)

Asking the Questions: _____

Answering the Questions: _____   _____ (10)

TOTAL SCORE: _____ (100)

Student's Name _____ I.D. Number _____

Course _____ Teacher _____ Date _____

Test Sections & Scoring Guidelines/Rubrics: **Score:**

A–H. MULTIPLE-CHOICE QUESTIONS

Help Wanted Ads
Grammar in Context: Job Interview Questions About Skills & Work History
Describing a Work Schedule
Grammar in Context: Calling In Sick & Late; Requesting a Schedule Change
An Employee Accident Report
Reading: A Paycheck Stub
Cloze Reading: Nonverbal Behavior at the Job Interview
Listening Assessment: A Job Interview

_____ correct x **2** points   _____ (80)

I. WRITING ASSESSMENT: Complete the Job Application Form

Score <u>globally</u> the student's ability to fill out the sections of the form requesting personal information, education experience, and employment experience:

Score **10** (Excellent), **8** (Good), **6** (Fair), **4** (Poor), or **2** (Unsatisfactory)

_____ (10)

J. SPEAKING ASSESSMENT

Score <u>separately</u> the student's ability to ask and answer the questions based on appropriateness, grammatical correctness, and comprehensibility:

Score **5** (Excellent), **4** (Good), **3** (Fair), **2** (Poor), or **1** (Unsatisfactory)

Asking the Questions: _____

Answering the Questions: _____   _____ (10)

TOTAL SCORE: _____ (100)

Student's Name _____   I.D. Number _____

Course _____   Teacher _____   Date _____

Test Sections & Scoring Guidelines/Rubrics: **Score:**

A–G. MULTIPLE-CHOICE QUESTIONS

First-Aid Kit
Grammar in Context: Calling 911
Grammar in Context: Describing a Suspect's Physical Characteristics to the Police
Reading: Warning Labels on Household Products
Reading: First-Aid Procedures
Learning Skill: Categorizing Words; Word Sets
Listening Assessment: An Emergency Call

_____ correct x **2** points   _____ (80)

H. WRITING ASSESSMENT: Fill Out the Form

For each of the following lines on the form:
Score **2** if completed with correct content and form/spelling.
Score **1** if completed with correct content but incorrect form/spelling.
Score **0** if incorrect or missing.

Name: _____

Height: _____

Weight: _____

Hair Color: _____

Eye Color: _____   _____ (10)

I. SPEAKING ASSESSMENT

Score <u>separately</u> the student's ability to ask and answer the questions based on appropriateness, grammatical correctness, and comprehensibility:

Score **5** (Excellent), **4** (Good), **3** (Fair), **2** (Poor), or **1** (Unsatisfactory)

Asking the Questions: _____

Answering the Questions: _____   _____ (10)

TOTAL SCORE: _____ (100)

Student's Name _____ I.D. Number _____

Course _____ Teacher _____ Date _____

Test Sections & Scoring Guidelines/Rubrics: Score:

A–E. MULTIPLE-CHOICE QUESTIONS

Housing Ads
Grammar in Context: Inquiring About Rentals
Grammar in Context: Describing Maintenance & Repairs Needed
   in a Rental Unit
Reading: A Floor Plan
Listening Assessment: Inquiring About a Rental Unit

_____ correct x **2** points   _____ (80)

F. WRITING ASSESSMENT

For each of the following criteria, score **2** (Good), **1** (Fair), or **0** (Unsatisfactory):

Appropriateness of Content: _____

Spelling: _____

Punctuation & Capitalization: _____

Grammar: _____

Completeness of Sentences: _____   _____ (10)

G. SPEAKING ASSESSMENT

Score <u>separately</u> the student's ability to ask and answer the questions based on appropriateness, grammatical correctness, and comprehensibility:

Score **5** (Excellent), **4** (Good), **3** (Fair), **2** (Poor), or **1** (Unsatisfactory)

Asking the Questions: _____

Answering the Questions: _____   _____ (10)

TOTAL SCORE: _____ (100)

Student's Name _____ I.D. Number _____

Course _____ Teacher _____ Date _____

Test Sections & Scoring Guidelines/Rubrics: **Score:**

A–I. MULTIPLE-CHOICE QUESTIONS

Identifying Parts of the Face & Body
Common Symptoms
Grammar in Context: Calling to Report an Absence; Making a Doctor Appointment
Procedures During a Medical Exam
Common Prescription & Non-Prescription Medications
Reading: Medicine Label Dosages
Reading: Medicine Label Instructions
Cloze Reading: A Note to the Teacher
Listening Assessment: Making a Doctor Appointment

_____ correct x **2** points   _____ (80)

J. WRITING ASSESSMENT: Fill Out the Medical History Form

Score <u>globally</u> the student's ability to fill out the various sections of the form:
Score **10** (Excellent), **8** (Good), **6** (Fair), **4** (Poor), or **2** (Unsatisfactory)

_____ (10)

K. SPEAKING ASSESSMENT

Score <u>separately</u> the student's ability to ask and answer the questions based on appropriateness, grammatical correctness, and comprehensibility:

Score **5** (Excellent), **4** (Good), **3** (Fair), **2** (Poor), or **1** (Unsatisfactory)

Asking the Questions: _____

Answering the Questions: _____   _____ (10)

TOTAL SCORE: _____ (100)

Student's Name _____	I.D. Number _____
Course _____ Teacher _____	Date _____

Test Sections & Scoring Guidelines/Rubrics: **Score:**

A–G. MULTIPLE-CHOICE QUESTIONS

Fahrenheit & Celsius Temperatures
Temperature Values
Grammar in Context: Beginning & Ending a Telephone Conversation
Reading: Telephone Directory White Pages
Reading: Telephone Directory Government Pages & Yellow Pages
Cloze Reading: Phone Messages
Listening Assessment: Recorded Telephone Information

_____ correct x **2** points   _____ (80)

H. WRITING ASSESSMENT

For each of the following criteria, score **2** (Good), **1** (Fair), or **0** (Unsatisfactory):

Appropriateness of content: _____

Spelling: _____

Punctuation & Capitalization: _____

Grammar: _____

Completeness of Sentences: _____

_____ (10)

I. SPEAKING ASSESSMENT

Score <u>separately</u> the student's ability to ask and answer the questions based on appropriateness, grammatical correctness, and comprehensibility:

Score **5** (Excellent), **4** (Good), **3** (Fair), **2** (Poor), or **1** (Unsatisfactory)

Asking the Questions: _____

Answering the Questions: _____   _____ (10)

TOTAL SCORE: _____ (100)

SIDE BY SIDE PLUS
Learner Assessment Record

Student's Name _____ I.D. Number _____

Course _____ Teacher _____ Date _____

Test Sections & Scoring Guidelines/Rubrics: Score:

A–E. MULTIPLE-CHOICE QUESTIONS

Household Repair Problems
Grammar in Context: Securing Household Repair Services
Reading: A TV Schedule
Cloze Reading: Household Repairs & Pronoun Review
Listening Assessment: Recorded Telephone Instructions

_____ correct x **2** points   _____ (80)

F. SKILL ASSESSMENT: Making a Schedule

Score <u>globally</u> the student's ability to fill out the chart as completely as possible:

Score **10** (Excellent), **8** (Good), **6** (Fair), **4** (Poor), or **2** (Unsatisfactory)

_____ (10)

G. SPEAKING ASSESSMENT

Score <u>separately</u> the student's ability to ask and answer the questions based on appropriateness, grammatical correctness, and comprehensibility:

Score **5** (Excellent), **4** (Good), **3** (Fair), **2** (Poor), or **1** (Unsatisfactory)

Asking the Questions: _____

Answering the Questions: _____   _____ (10)

TOTAL SCORE: _____ (100)

SIDE BY SIDE PLUS
Learner Progress Chart

BOOK 2

Student's Name _____ I.D. Number _____

Course _____ Teacher _____ Term _____

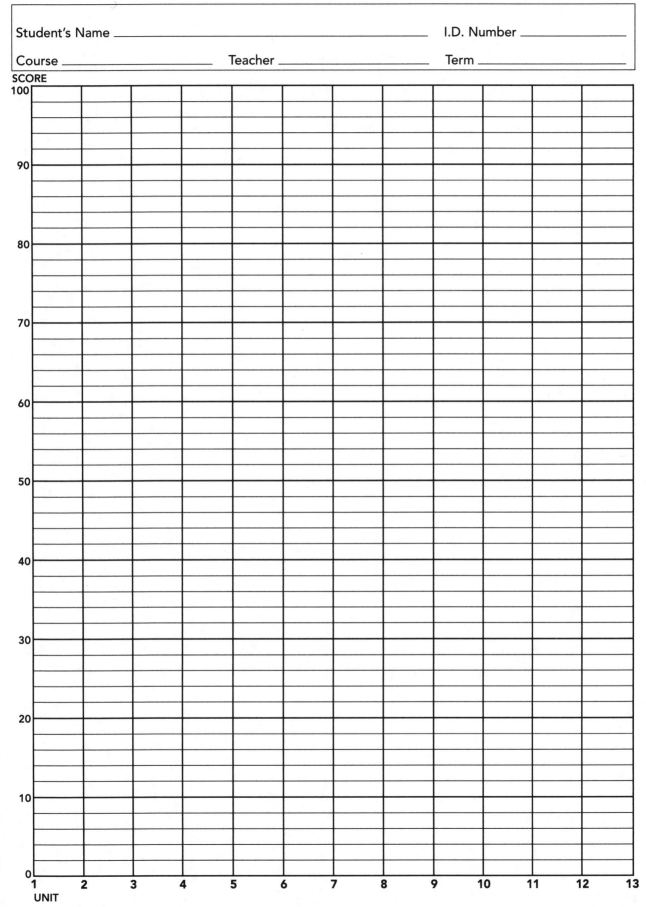

SCORE

100

90

80

70

60

50

40

30

20

10

0

1 2 3 4 5 6 7 8 9 10 11 12 13

UNIT

© 2008 Pearson Education, Inc.